Kids Can Share

Creative lessons for teaching compassion, respect and responsibility

Written by Rhoda Orszag Vestuto and Doris Larsen

Illustrated by April Hartmann

tlc

Teaching & Learning Company

1204 Buchanan St., P.O. Box 10

Carthage, IL 62321-0010

This book belongs to

____

Dedication

We dedicate this book with love to our children, Cecily, Chris, Dan, Laura, Christie, Susan; our grandchildren, Kevin, Lindsey, Jeremey, Andrea, Evan, Erika; our great grandchildren, Kieren, Maxwell, Annabelle, Landon; and to children everywhere.

Acknowledgment

We are deeply grateful to Chris Vestuto for his insights, suggestions, support and editing. Thank you, Chris!

Cover art by April Hartman

ISBN No. 1-57310-384-5

Printing No. 987654321

Teaching & Learning Company
1204 Buchanan St., P.O. Box 10
Carthage, IL 62321-0010

Table of Contents

Dear Teacher or Parent,

Kids Can Share was written for the teacher, parent educator, caregiver or any parent who is looking for materials that foster social values. Each chapter contains a set of activities that concentrate on a specific ethical issue. These activities will motivate children to practice acts of kindness, compassion, respect, responsibility, etc.

Kids Can Share is innovative and easy to use:

- It includes all necessary patterns and samples.
- It contains fun activities appropriate for preschoolers, kindergartners and special education students.
- It includes unique features using hands-on activities and real-life scenarios.
- It is organized so that each activity can be implemented independently or linked together by chapter or unit.
- It utilizes a method that eliminates power struggles between the child and the adult.

Sincerely,

Rhoda Doris

Rhoda Orszag Vestuto & Doris Larsen

Unit 1

Within Myself

Emotional Growth

Little Jack Horner
Sat in a corner,
Eating a Christmas pie;
He put in his thumb,
And pulled out a plum,
And said, "What a good boy am I!"

—*Mother Goose*

Chapter 1
Hatch a Heartasaurus

Problems

- Not sharing.
- Pushing other children around.
- Generally insensitive to others.
- Instigating situations which may cause peers to get into trouble.
- Excessive bossiness.

Goals

- Increase sensitivity to people's feelings.
- Demonstrate kindness, caring and generosity.
- Experience the rewards of friendship.

Chapter 1
Hatch a Heartasaurus

Ways & Means

Discover a Heartasaurus

- Premake a Heartasaurus and an egg for each child. (See patterns on pages 8-9.) Display the closed eggs, each containing a Heartasaurus, in one large nest made with packing straw or the kind of "grass" used in baskets. These may be displayed on a bulletin board. (One large Heartasaurus and egg may be used for an entire group in lieu of individual ones.)
- Discuss with the children the fact that dinosaurs are extinct except for the few Heartasaurus eggs that we have found. Ask them if they know what eggs need in order to hatch. Guide the children to the conclusion that eggs need to be kept warm over a period of time. Go on to explain that Heartasaurus eggs need a special warmth that can come only from acts of kindness.

Model/Role Play

- Act out situations that demonstrate the goals and contrast them with situations that demonstrate problems such as:

1. Inviting peers to join in activities versus excluding some peers from play, parties, etc.
2. Sharing toys or possessions willingly, when appropriate, versus grabbing and not sharing. (Be sure that this is age appropriate.)
3. Engaging in cooperative play versus destroying peers' products (e.g., block or sand building).
4. Focusing on own work versus excessive interfering with peers' work or being bossy.

Hatch a Heartasaurus

- Each day observe, define and praise the children's efforts and progress toward the goals. Reinforce growth by opening individual eggs a crack. On successive days, as the eggs gradually open, each baby Heartasaurus slowly begins to appear. The "incubation" period should take a minimum of two weeks to complete.

Culmination

- Give the children their newly hatched Heartasauruses along with "feedbags." (The feedbags are made of sandwich bags filled with appropriate treats.) The children may "help" their Heartasaurus eat its "food" supply.

Reinforcement

- If review is necessary, new eggs may be "discovered" and the activity repeated.

Name ______________________________

Chapter 1
Hatch a Heartasaurus

Heartasaurus Pattern

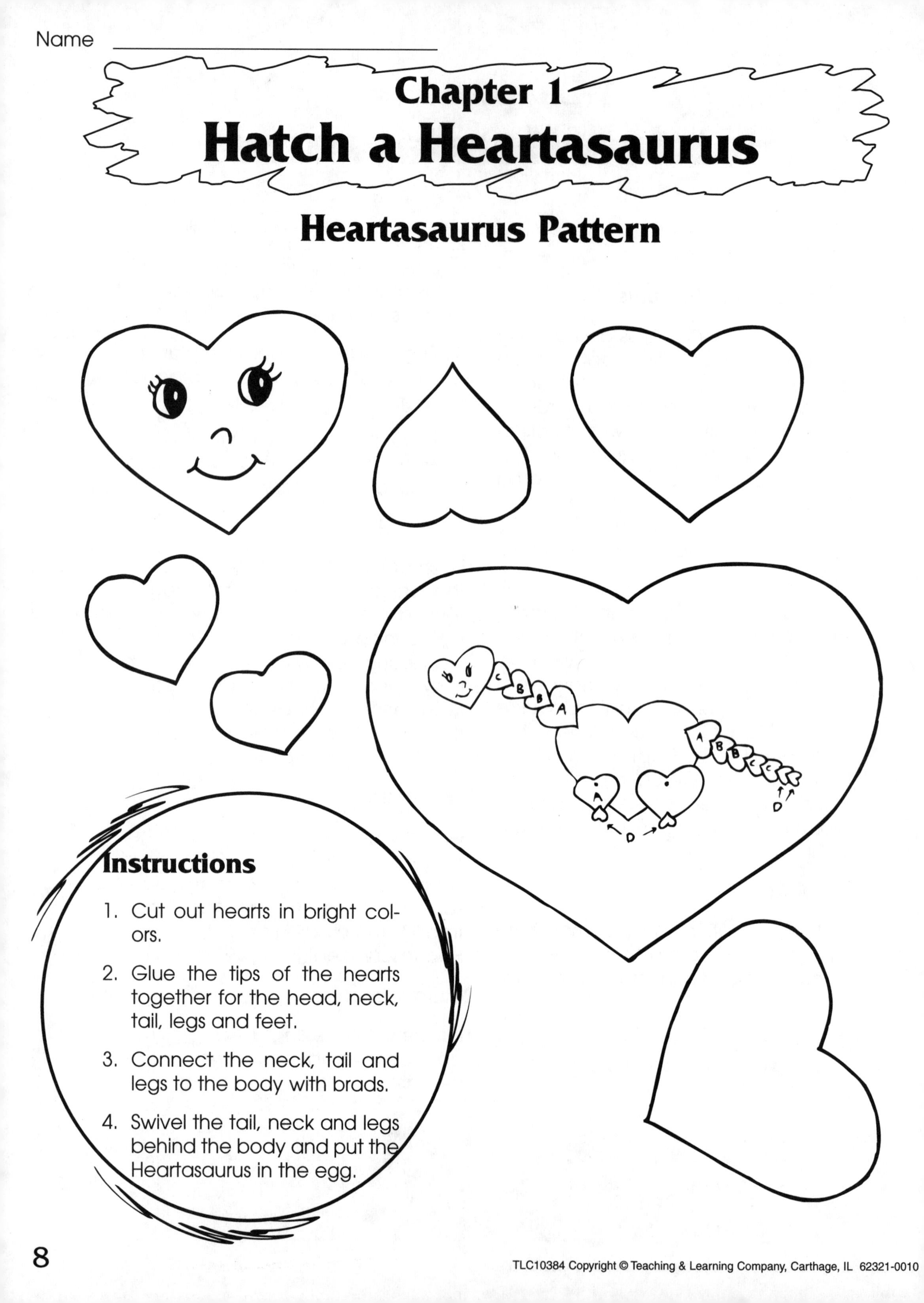

Instructions

1. Cut out hearts in bright colors.
2. Glue the tips of the hearts together for the head, neck, tail, legs and feet.
3. Connect the neck, tail and legs to the body with brads.
4. Swivel the tail, neck and legs behind the body and put the Heartasaurus in the egg.

Name ____________________

Chapter 1
Hatch a Heartasaurus

Heartasaurus Egg Pattern

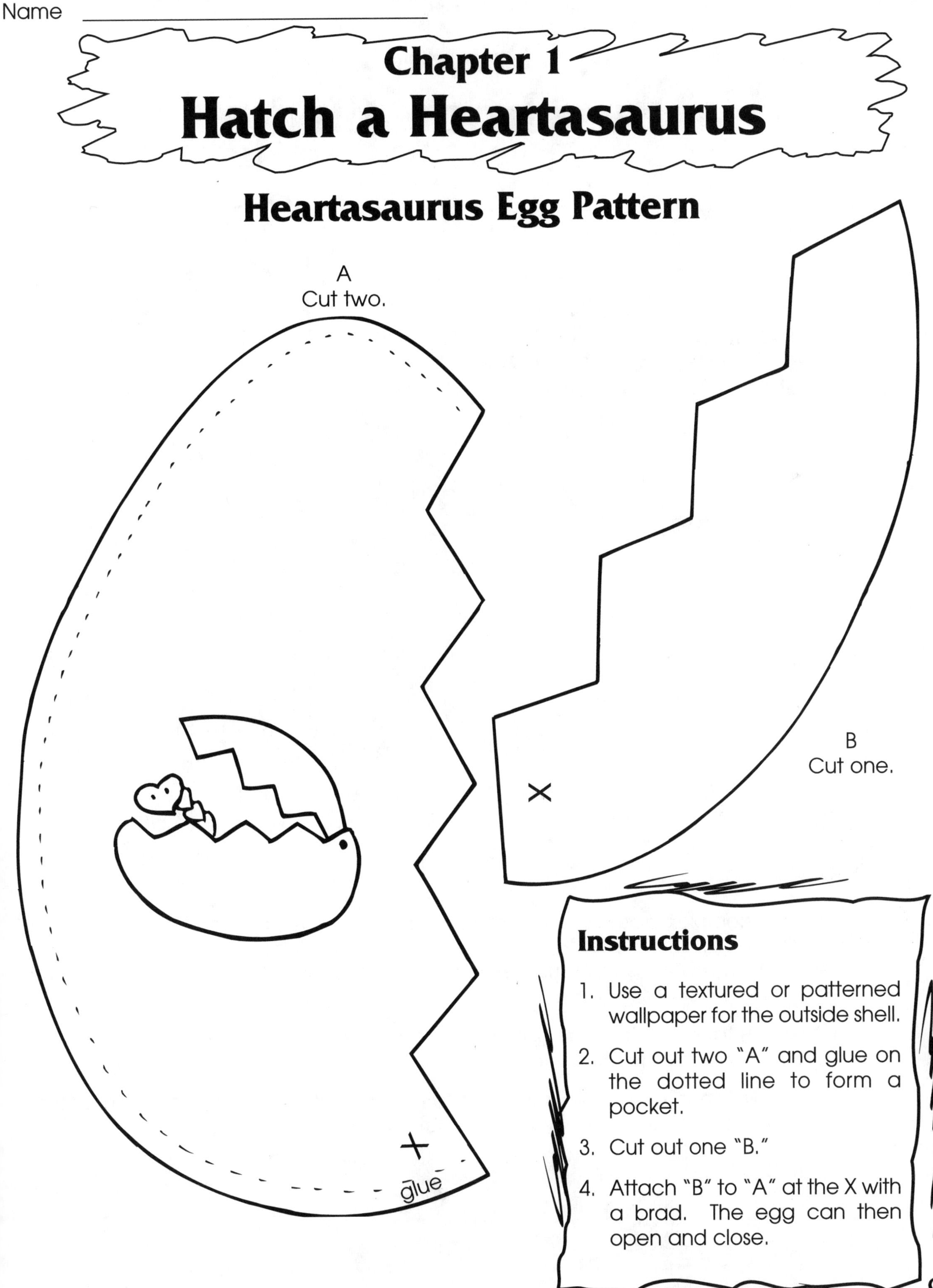

Instructions

1. Use a textured or patterned wallpaper for the outside shell.
2. Cut out two "A" and glue on the dotted line to form a pocket.
3. Cut out one "B."
4. Attach "B" to "A" at the X with a brad. The egg can then open and close.

Chapter 2
Busybody Birdie

Problem

- Frequent complaining about others; especially tattling.

Goals

- Report to an adult when there is a dangerous situation (rock throwing, fighting, etc.).
- Increase ability to handle situations independently when appropriate.
- Learn skills related to problem solving.
- Use good judgement.

Note

This is a most complex issue because different adults will have different interpretations of what tattling really is. An effective method of handling each situation is to simply have individual children ask, "Is this tattling?" when reporting an incident. Based upon your judgement, your response will be:

"Yes, it is tattling." Take this opportunity to discuss ways children could handle the situation independently.

"No, that's not tattling. It's important to tell me that." Take this opportunity to discuss why it's important for an adult to get involved.

Chapter 2
Busybody Birdie

Ways & Means

Save the Peacock

- Read the children "The Story of Busybody Birdie." It may be presented as a flannel board story. (See patterns on pages 15-16.)

Peacock Project

- Give each child a peacock with the sad face attached and an envelope filled with feathers that have fallen off. The children will receive one feather from their envelope each day that they demonstrate growth in this area. Remember that they must preface the reporting of a situation with: "Is this tattling?"
- One large peacock may be used for an entire group in lieu of individual birds.

Culmination

- Give children their special little peacocks fully feathered and wearing happy faces.
- If individual birds are not used, give or "mail" each child a peacock card. (See pattern on page 14.)

Reinforcement

- If review is necessary, the peacock feathers again "drop off," as in the story, and the activity repeated.

Chapter 2
Busybody Birdie

The Story of Busybody Birdie

Once upon a time there was a little peacock. He had the coolest, most awesome tail in town. His many friends admired it and that made him very proud, indeed.

As time went on, his pride grew until he thought he was the most important bird around. He became so vain that he felt he always knew best and he began to stick his beak in where it didn't belong. That's when his friends gave him the name Busybody Birdie. But that didn't stop the little peacock; he made matters even worse by starting to tattle!

Do you know what tattling is? (Solicit ideas from the children.) Sometimes you need to tell a grown-up when somebody throws rocks or sand, gets hurt or when something happens that is dangerous. That is not tattling. But do you know what Busybody Birdie did? He whined and complained about any old thing. He would say things like: "She's not listening." "He won't give me his toy." "She has mud on her shoes." Busybody Birdie was tattling.

Now, back to Busybody Birdie's story. He began to tattle so often that he became known as Busybody Birdie the Tattle-Tail. Speaking of tails, his coolest-most-awesome-tail-in-town started to droop and drag. One day, as the little peacock was busy tattling, a tail feather dropped right on the ground (begin to remove tail feathers). Uh-oh! The next day and the next, every time he tattled, another feather fell. Finally, poor Busybody Birdie the Tattle-Tail was Busybody Birdie the Tattle-Tail-Less. (Change to peacock's sad face.)

Chapter 2

Busybody Birdie

What a shame! The little peacock felt awful, and he knew that he had lost all his feathers because of his tattling. He was even sadder when he figured out that he had lost all his friends as well as his tail. He didn't feel very important anymore and he wanted his friends back. What could he do?

You can help him! Here's how: When you feel you need to tell a grown-up about something that happens, first ask "Is this tattling?" You will learn whether it's important for the grown-up to handle a situation or if you can handle it by yourself. The little peacock will be watching and learning along with you about tattling. You can be the first friend he's had in quite a while.

And now, let me tell you the best surprise of all. As you remember to check about tattling, day by day, feather by feather, the little peacock will get his tail back . . . and it will, again, be the coolest, most awesome tail in town. Most importantly, he will have his friends back and they no longer will call him Busybody Birdie the Tattle-Tail . . . thanks to you!

The End

For Discussion

Why will the little peacock have his friends back?

What do you think his friends will call him now?

Can you give him a new name?

Name
Chapter 2
Busybody Birdie
Little Peacock Card Sample
Thank you for being my friend!

Name ____________________

Chapter 2
Busybody Birdie

Busybody Birdie Pattern

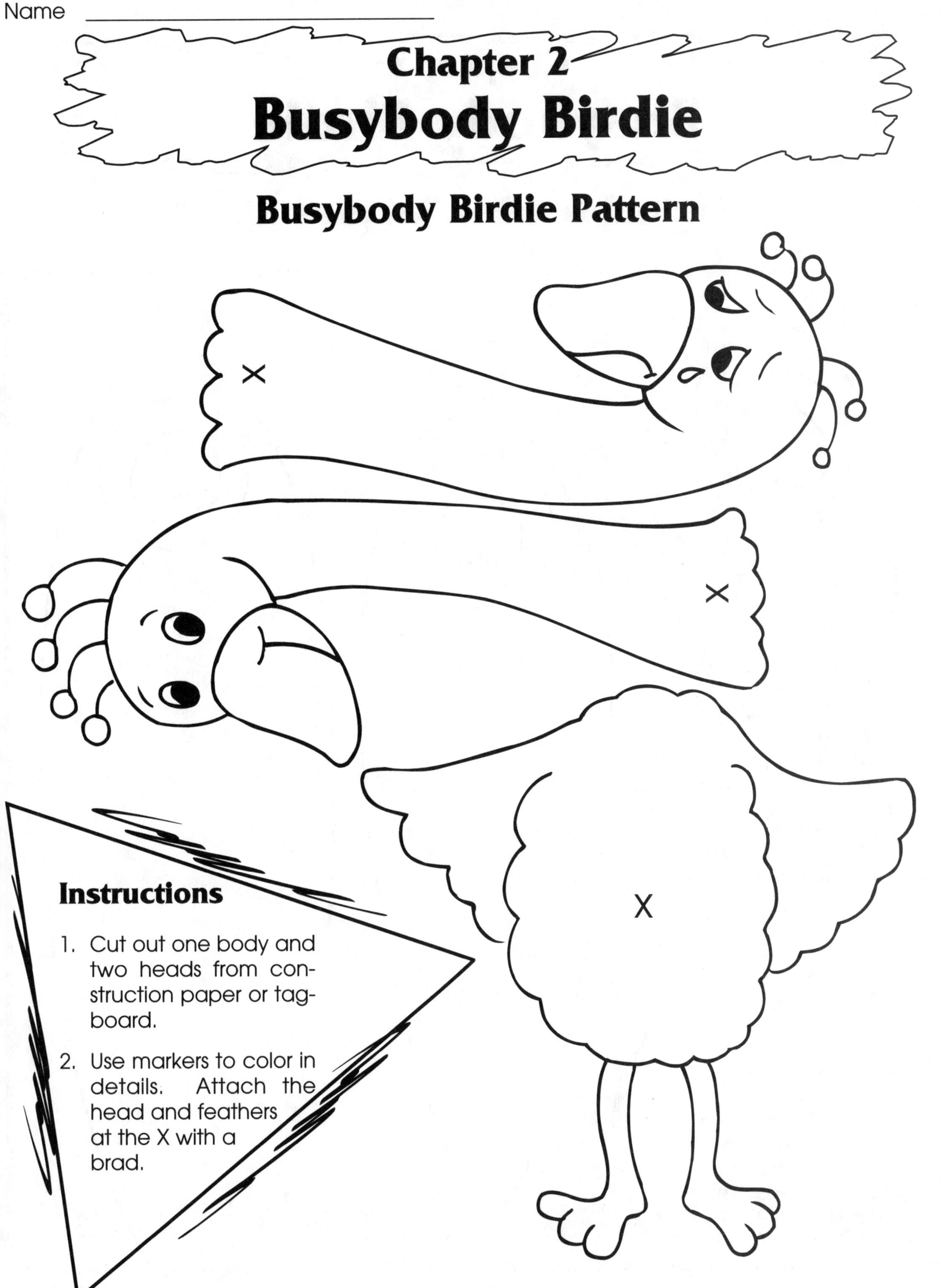

Instructions

1. Cut out one body and two heads from construction paper or tagboard.
2. Use markers to color in details. Attach the head and feathers at the X with a brad.

Name ______________________________

Chapter 2
Busybody Birdie

Tail Feather Patterns

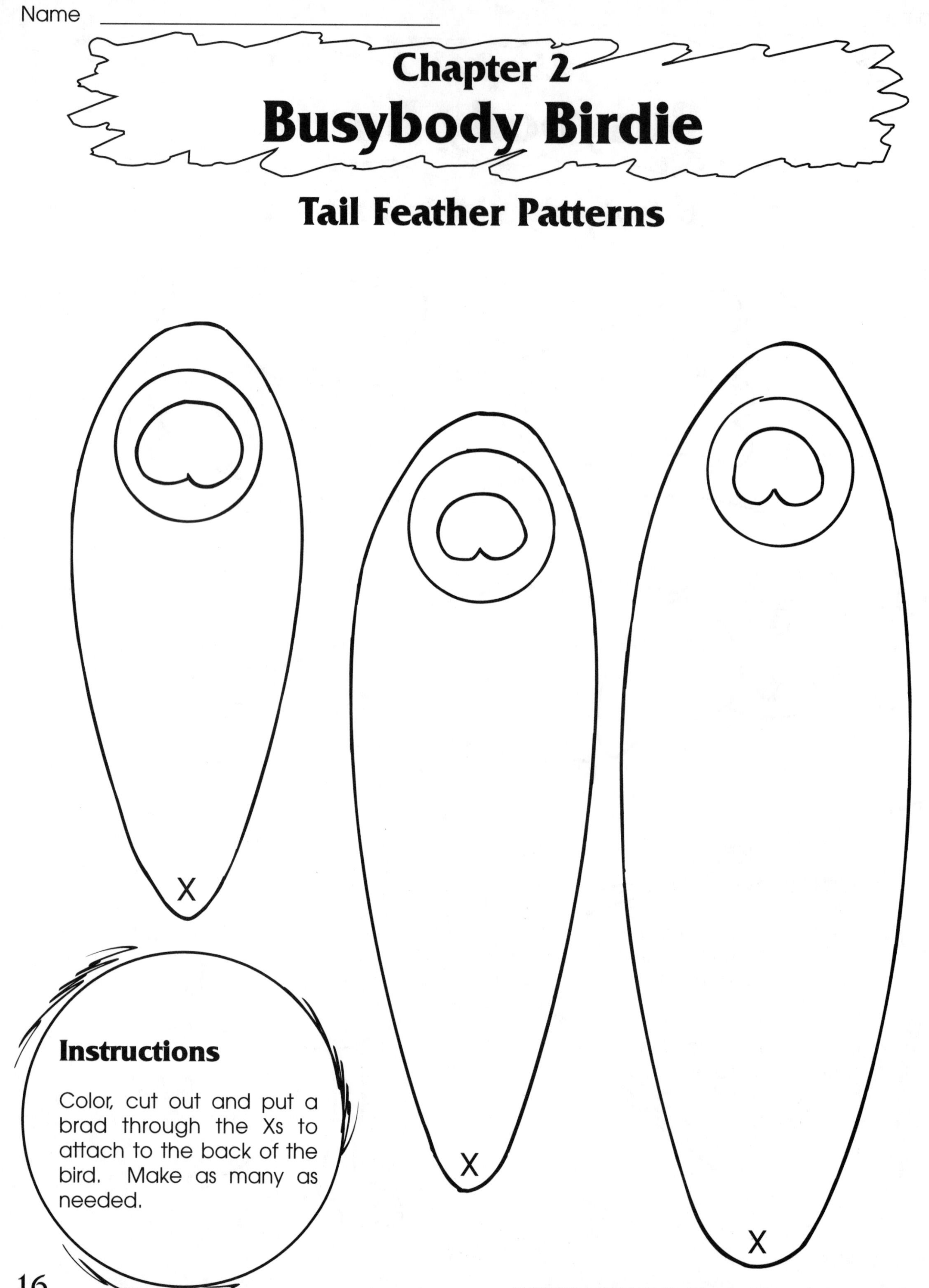

Instructions

Color, cut out and put a brad through the Xs to attach to the back of the bird. Make as many as needed.

Chapter 3
FOPNOF Club

Food On Plate Not On Floor

Problem

- Excessive messiness and carelessness while eating.

Goals

- Become more careful at meal or snack time.
- Reduce amount of food dropped.
- Take responsibility for cleaning up after self.

Chapter 3
FOPNOF Club

Food On Plate Not On Floor

Ways & Means

Join the Club

- Introduce the FOPNOF Club, an exclusive club for children who learn to keep their Food On Plate Not On Floor.

1. Explain membership requirements to the children. (See Goals on page 17.)
2. Show the children a paper plate or school lunch tray along with an assortment of collage items (yarn, plastic or wood scraps, small pieces of drinking straws, tissue paper, cotton balls or any other small pieces* of "junk"). Tell them that, after each meal, they may glue one collage item on their individual plates or trays as a symbol of their efforts to meet the goals.
3. After mealtime, ask the children individually "Are you a FOPNOFer?" and have them show you their eating area. Teach, praise efforts and reward collage items as appropriate.

Culmination

- Collages may be considered completed and membership cards issued when children consistently take responsibility for cleaning up their eating areas independently. (See pattern on page 19.)

"Mascot" Model (optional)

- Set up a stuffed animal or doll with a napkin around its neck and an eating area with a "place setting." Mascot should have access to the collage tray and a paper plate to complete. Each day place some plastic food, pictures of food or real food on the mascot's plate or on the "floor." Children then determine whether or not the mascot is a FOPNOFer and "help" to glue a collage item onto its plate, if appropriate.

Reinforcement

- If review is necessary, repeat FOPNOF Club activity and issue membership renewals by adding a sticker to the original card.

*Remember that children like to put things in their mouths. Take care that no item is used that could present a choking hazard.

Name ______________________

Chapter 3
FOPNOF Club

Food On Plate Not On Floor

FOPNOF Membership Cards

FOPNOP CLUB

Food On Plate Not On Floor

Membership Card

______________________ Name

______________________ Date Issued

____

______________________ Address

______________________ Signature

Instructions

The card may be covered with clear, self-adhesive plastic or laminated.

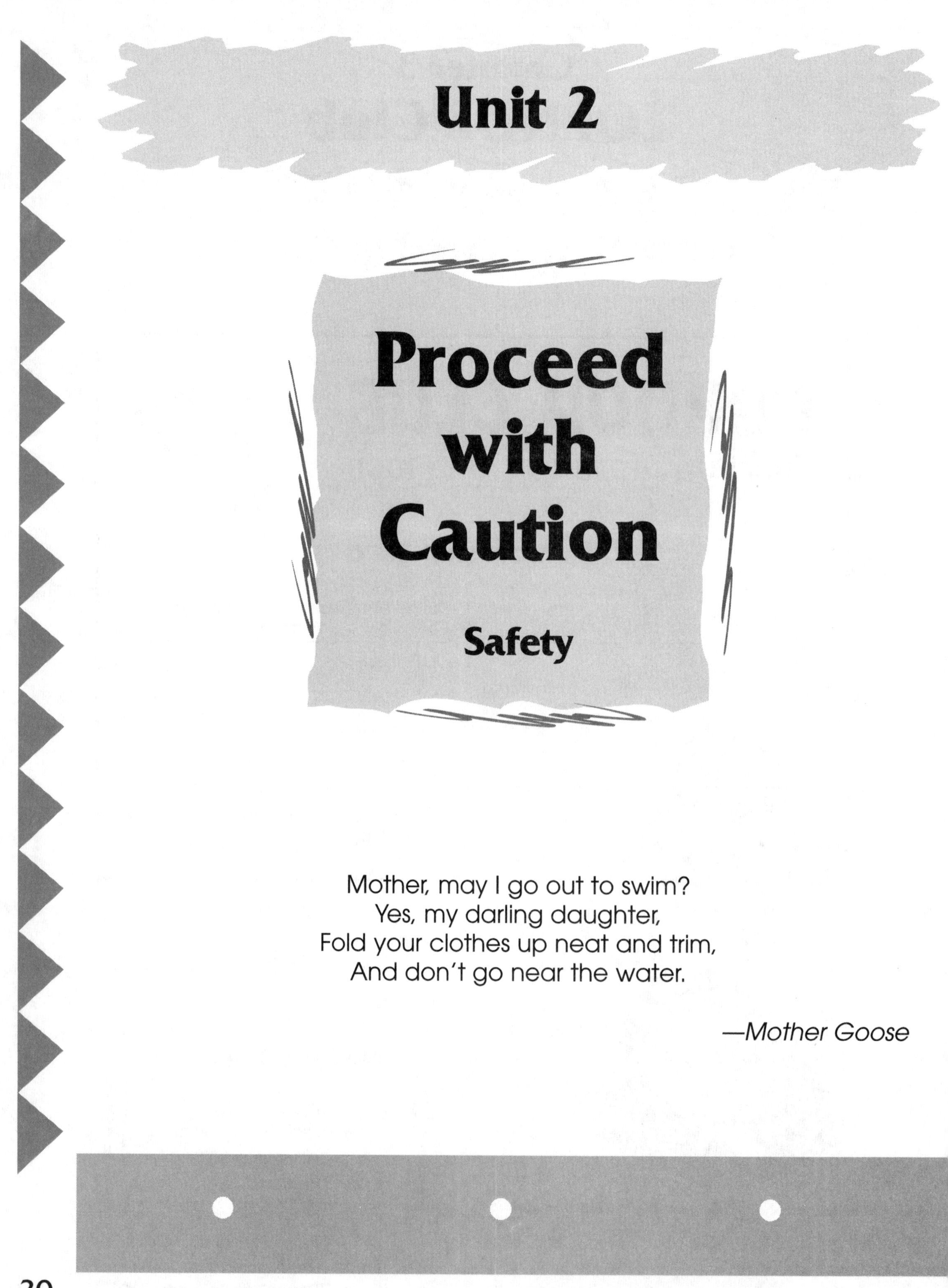

Unit 2

Proceed with Caution

Safety

Mother, may I go out to swim?
Yes, my darling daughter,
Fold your clothes up neat and trim,
And don't go near the water.

—Mother Goose

Chapter 4
Careful Bear

Chapter 4 is designed to be used in conjunction with Chapters 5-8. Safety is such a broad subject that Chapters 5-8 are set up to address four major areas critical for young children (Street Safety, Car/Bus Safety, Personal Safety and Safety with Others). They are sequenced, each building upon the next, to effect real learning in these areas. Chapter 4 contains materials and samples needed to tie all four safety issues into one unit.

Ways & Means

Earn a Merit Badge

- Introduce children, in a general manner, to all four areas of safety. (Refer to Chapters 5-8.) Then show them a completed banner displaying all the merit badges that they may earn. (See page 22-23 for directions and patterns.)

  1. Prepare a banner. Children should do as much cutting and assembling as their abilities allow.
  2. Premake badges and place in individual envelopes.
  3. Display children's banners on a bulletin board or in another prominent place.
  4. Award appropriate badges as they are earned. Then have the children glue them on their banner.

Culmination

- Present the children with their banner containing all of their badges. The presentation should be made in a manner that communicates recognition of their achievements.
- Give or send the children special "mail" from Careful Bear. (See pages 24-25 for patterns and directions.)

"Mascot" Model (optional)

- Display stuffed bear, seated on a chair, wearing or holding a banner containing all of the badges that can be earned. The bear may wear a hat with the name "Careful Bear" on the front.

Reinforcement

- If review is necessary, begin by repeating "mail" from Careful Bear.

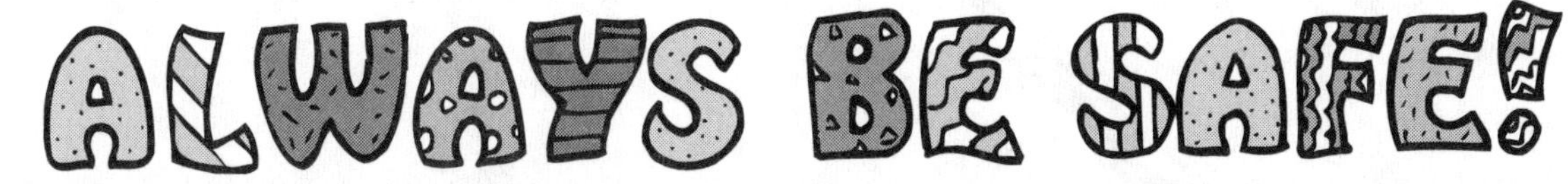

Name ______________________________

Chapter 4
Careful Bear

Banner

Suggested Materials: construction paper, burlap or felt, craft stick or dowel

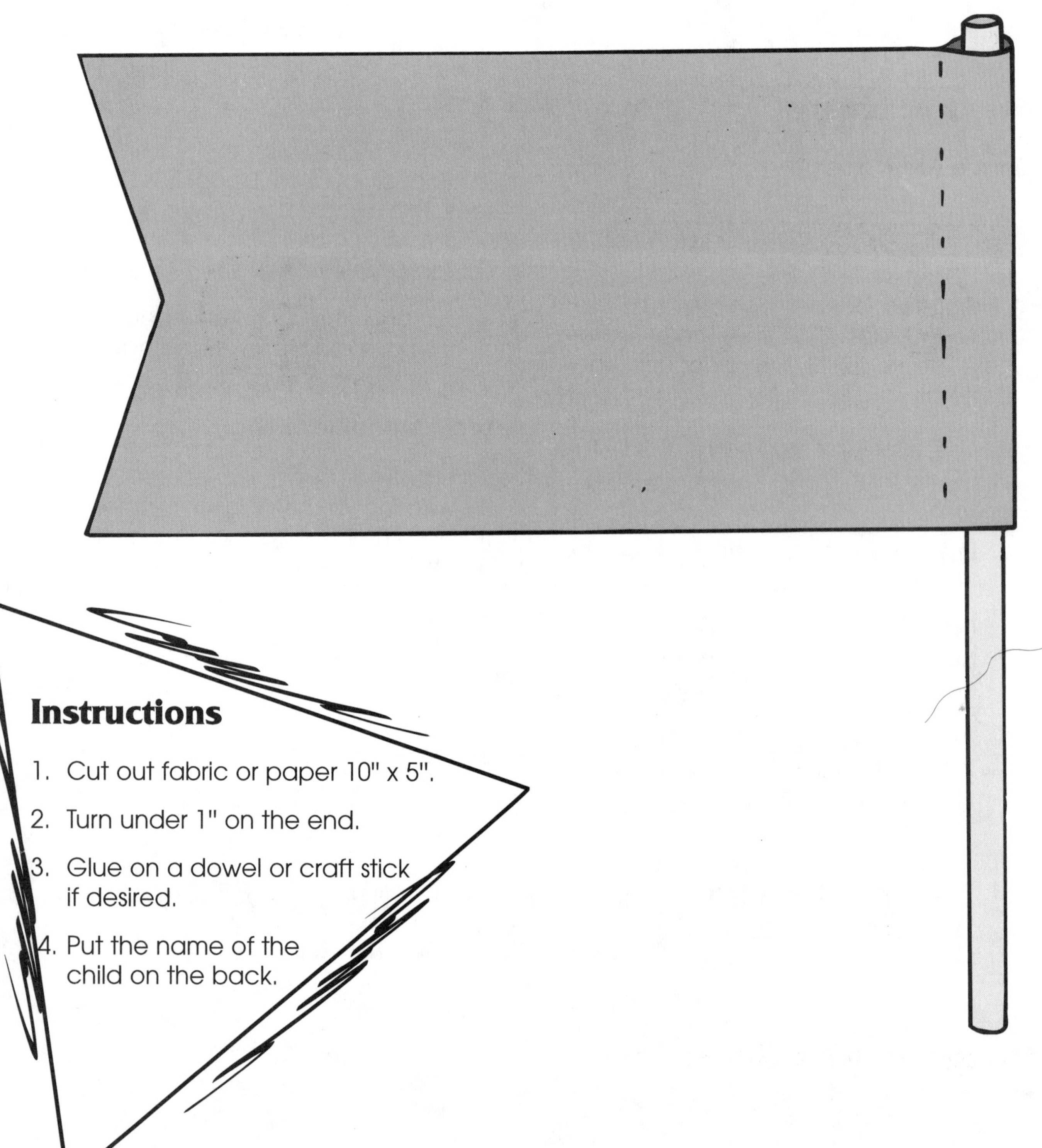

Instructions

1. Cut out fabric or paper 10" x 5".
2. Turn under 1" on the end.
3. Glue on a dowel or craft stick if desired.
4. Put the name of the child on the back.

Name ____________________

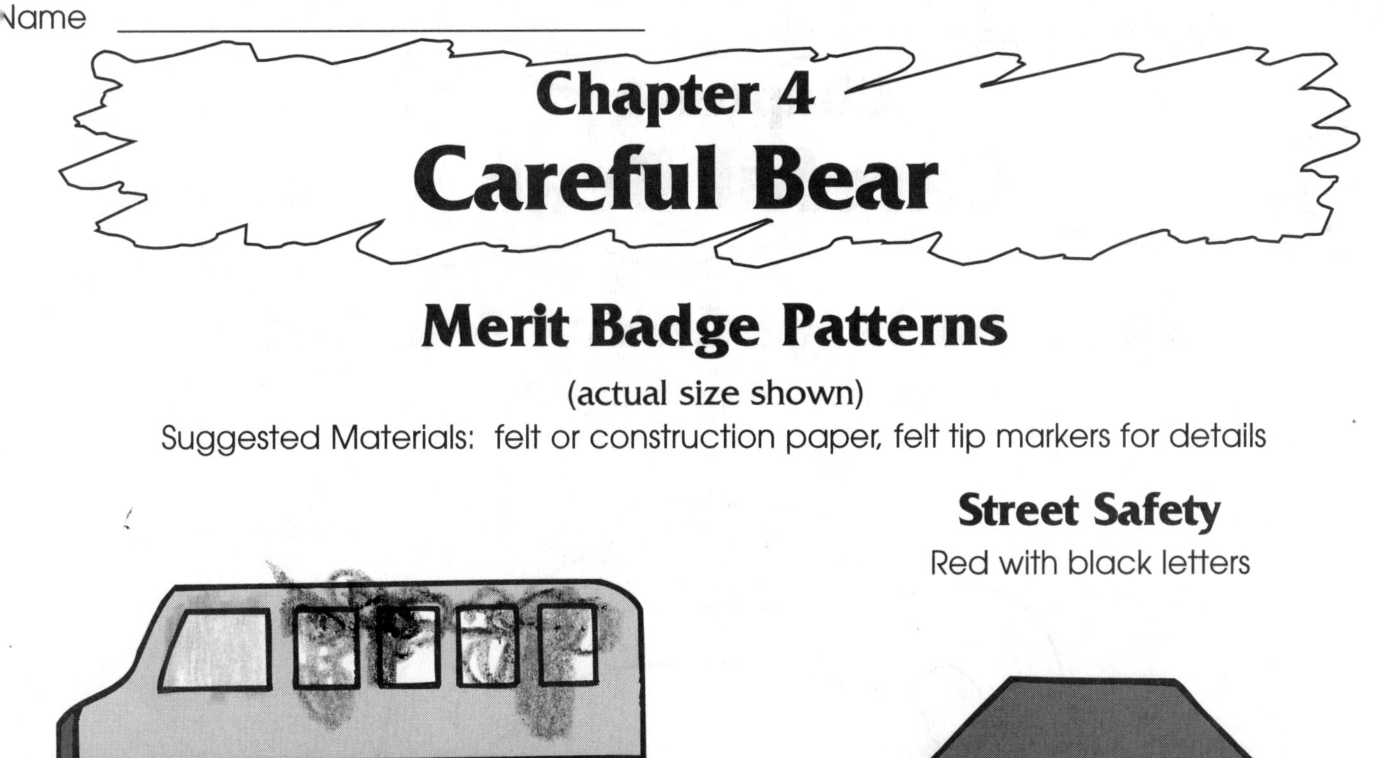

Chapter 4
Careful Bear

Merit Badge Patterns

(actual size shown)

Suggested Materials: felt or construction paper, felt tip markers for details

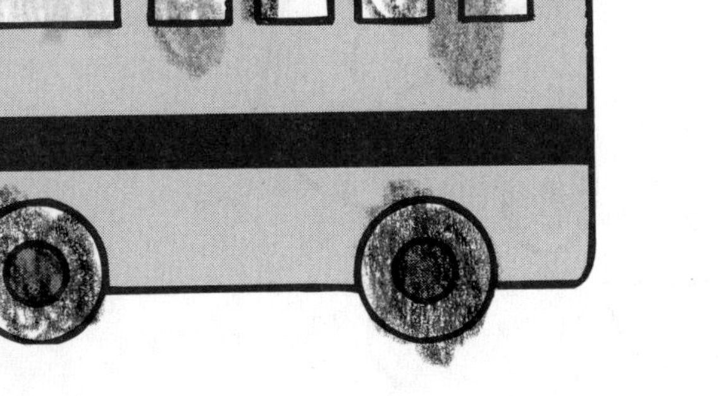

Car/Bus Safety
Yellow with black details

Safety with Others
Black silhouettes

Street Safety
Red with black letters

STOP

Personal Safety
Neutral with black details

Name ______________________

Chapter 4
Careful Bear

Pattern for Large Careful Bear Letter

(See instructions on page 26.)

Name ______________________________

Chapter 4
Careful Bear

Pattern for Small Careful Bear Letter

(See instructions on page 26.)

Chapter 4
Careful Bear

Instructions for Large Careful Bear Letter

1. Accordion fold paper and trace large bear pattern on front.
2. Cut around bear while folded, then open. (There will be five bears connected at the paws, like paper dolls.)
3. Add details to each bear.
4. Refold and insert letter in an envelope made by folding a 9" x 12" paper in half and taping at sides.
5. Address to children and use any kind of sticker to simulate postage.

Optional: Run large bears on copying machine and join at paws with tape.

Instructions for Small Careful Bear Letter

1. Use a copying machine to run pattern.
2. Accordion fold and leave as is or cut around the bears.
3. Insert in an envelope.
4. Address to children and use any kind of stamp to simulate postage.

Optional: Color bears before putting in an envelope.

Chapter 5
Street Safety

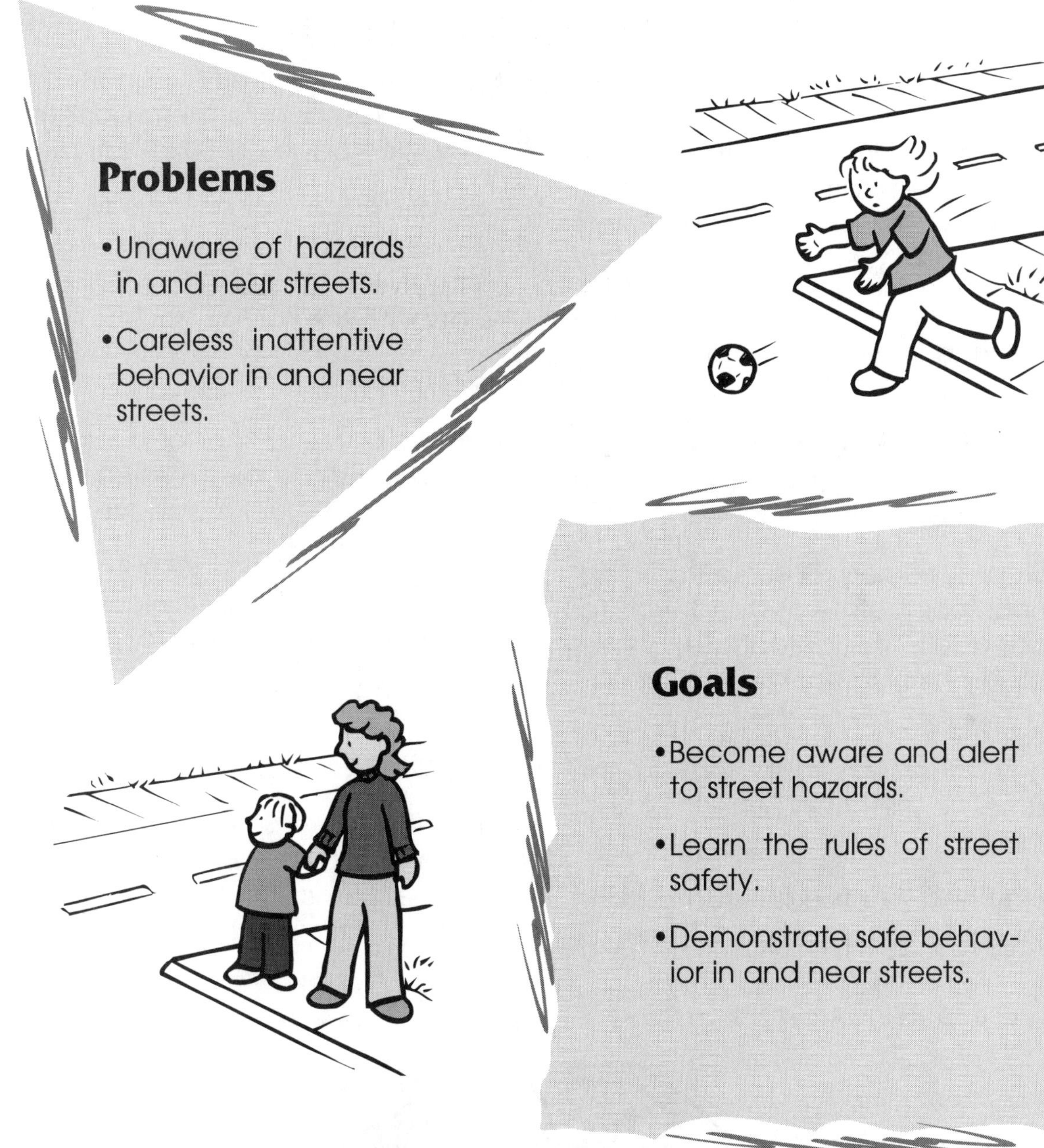

Problems

- Unaware of hazards in and near streets.
- Careless inattentive behavior in and near streets.

Goals

- Become aware and alert to street hazards.
- Learn the rules of street safety.
- Demonstrate safe behavior in and near streets.

Note

Taking the ages and levels of responsibility of the children into account, the goals may range from never going into the street unless accompanied by an adult to independently crossing, retrieving a ball, walking a bike across, etc.

Chapter 5
Street Safety

Ways & Means

Earn a Merit Badge

- Introduce the children to the specific area of street safety and tell them that they may earn a Street Safety Merit Badge. (See page 23 for pattern.)

Model/Role Play

- Act out situations which demonstrate safe and unsafe behaviors in streets, parking lots and driveways. Some examples would be:

  1. Stop at corners, observe traffic signals, look both ways and wait for an adult, if appropriate, versus blindly running out into the street.
  2. Ask the adult to retrieve a ball or any other toy that goes in the street versus running after it without thinking.
  3. Stay next to an adult in a parking lot versus running ahead alone.

Rules of the Road

1. Children make traffic signals and learn to respond to them appropriately. (See pages 29-30 for samples.)
2. Use premade signals or say, "red light, green light, yellow light" so that the children may practice appropriate responses when they are occupied with games, rhythms, riding trikes, etc.
3. Invite a police officer or a crossing guard to talk to the children. (The police department may have safety coloring booklets.)
4. Take advantage of any outings or plan walking field trips to practice and observe progress towards independent street safety.

Culmination

- Award the Street Safety Merit Badge. If a banner is being used, the children may glue it on at this time.

Name ______________________________

Traffic Light Coloring Page

Draw a line to the correct circle, then color it.

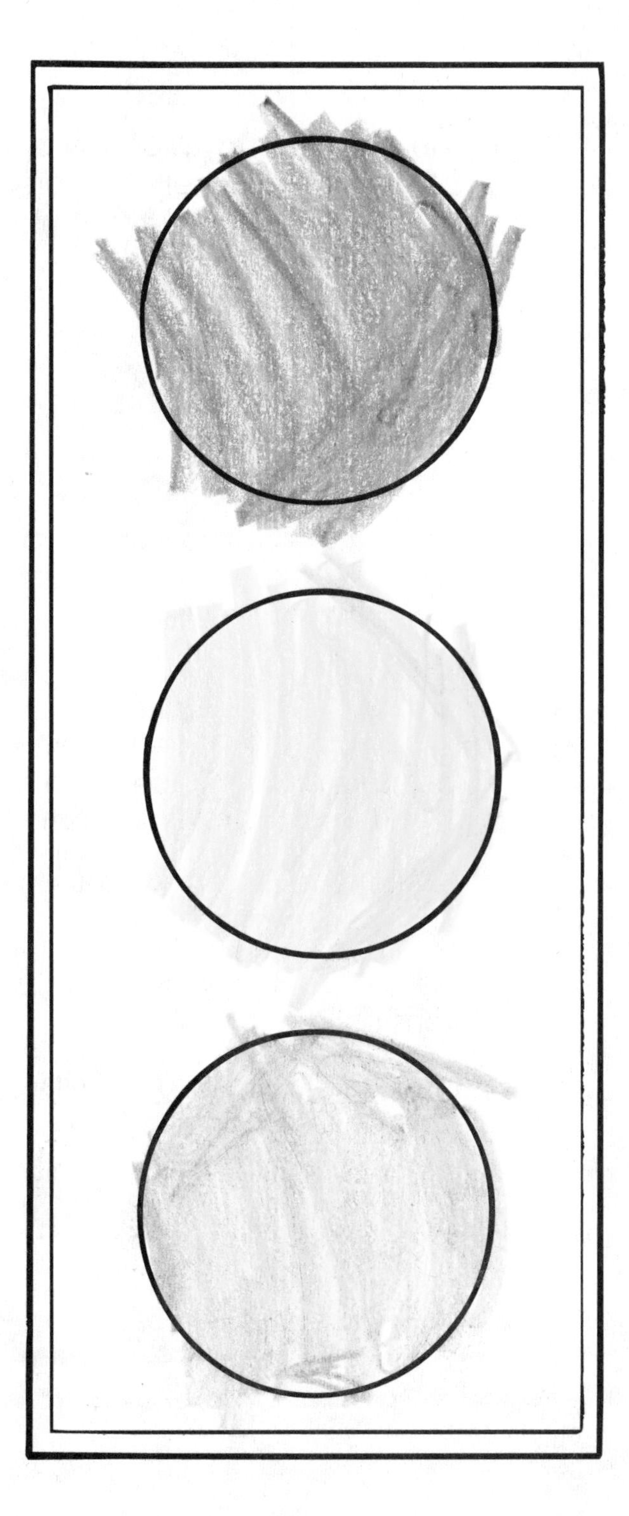

Yellow means **wait** for red
or **wait** for green.
It's the only color in between!

The color **red** is on the top.
When you see it,
you must **stop**!

Green means it's OK to **go**—
but you still need to look,
you know.

Chapter 5
Street Safety

Standard Street Signals

Children trace circles, squares and rectangle.

Children cut out circles, squares and rectangle.

Children glue circles on rectangle in the proper order.

Display on a bulletin board.

Optional: Make a two-sided signal and hang it as a mobile.

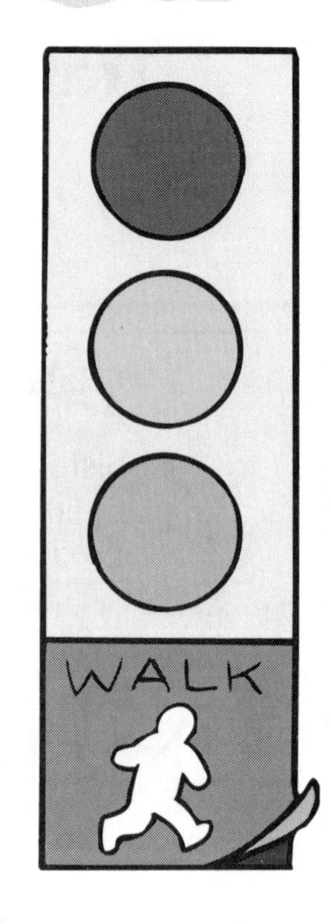

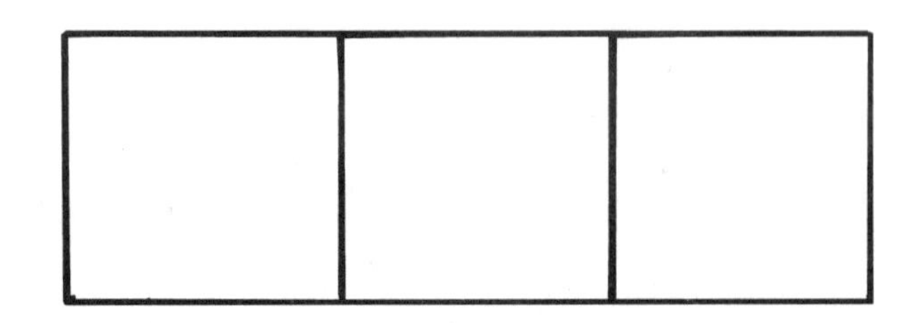

Changing Signals

Prepare black square and white rectangle as shown in diagram.

Divide white rectangle into three equal parts.

Children color or paint rectangle sections as shown.

Insert rectangle through slits so that signal can be changed.

Chapter 6
Car/Bus Safety

Problem

- Boisterous, wild or irresponsible behavior creating hazardous situations.

Goals

- Remain seated with seat belts fastened at all times.
- Keep hands, feet and possessions to self.
- Use your "inside voice." (Speak in moderate tones.)

Chapter 6
Car/Bus Safety

Ways & Means

Earn a Merit Badge

- Introduce the children to the specific area of car/bus safety and tell them that they may earn a Car/Bus Safety Merit Badge. (See page 23 for pattern.)

Model/Role Play

- Act out safe and unsafe behaviors which demonstrate situations that could occur in a car or bus. Some examples would be:

1. Maintain seat belt buckled at all times versus unbuckling belt and standing up, climbing or jumping.
2. Sit in a safe manner versus kicking, hitting, excessive wiggling or throwing objects.
3. Talk in moderate tones versus yelling or screaming.

"Pilot to Co-Pilot"

1. Set up a Car/Bus Center by arranging chairs to resemble the interior of a car or bus. Attach belts or yarn on chairs for use as seat belts. Provide a cap and "steering wheel" for the "driver." (Something as simple as a paper plate can be used as a "steering wheel.") The "driver" should encourage responsible behavior from his "passengers," which will help to expand his own understanding of the importance of car/bus safety.
2. Invite a local or school bus driver or parent to talk to the children from the driver's perspective.

Culmination

- Award the Car/Bus Safety Merit Badge. If a banner is being used, the children may glue it on at this time.

Chapter 7
Personal Safety

Problems

- Carelessness or lack of awareness of precautions to take in everyday environment.
- Lack of information related to correct procedures to use in emergency situations.

Goals

- Use caution with or keep hands away from:
  1. moving objects such as doors, machinery and escalators
  2. knives and other sharp objects
  3. matches, stoves, microwaves and other heat or steam-generating appliances
- Use good judgement:
  1. in determining acceptable versus unacceptable advances or touching by peers and adults
  2. in determining what is appropriate to put in the mouth or to eat
  3. when rocking in chairs, running, riding tricycles, etc.
- Follow correct procedures in:
  1. emergency situations such as fires and earthquakes
  2. moving away from and reporting unacceptable advances by peers or adults

Chapter 7
Personal Safety

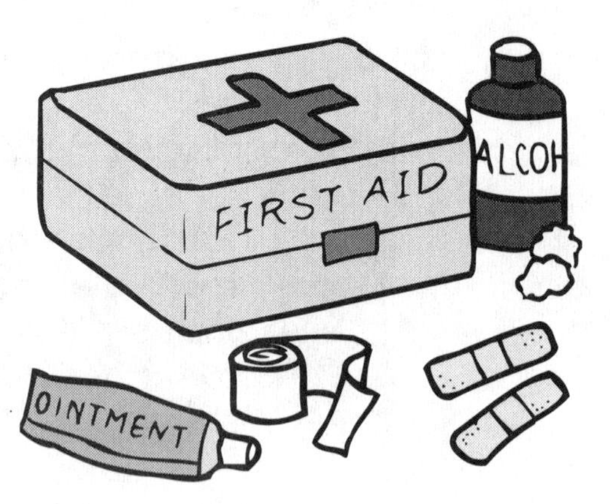

Ways & Means

Earn a Merit Badge

- Introduce the children to the specific area of personal safety and tell them that they may earn a Personal Safety Merit Badge. (See page 23 for pattern.)

Red Alert

1. Invite a fire fighter or a Red Cross representative to give a presentation to the children on emergency procedures. (Safety stickers, booklets, etc., are often available upon request.)
2. During routine activities, practice emergency procedures such as "Stop, Drop and Roll" for fires; "Duck, Cover and Hold" for earthquakes and calling 911 on a play phone for emergency situations.
3. Make arrangements to visit a fire station or a Red Cross Center.

Code Blue

1. Familiarize the children with a first aid kit so they understand that there are ways to take care of minor injuries.
2. Children make first aid kit samples. (See page 36.)
3. Invite a doctor or nurse to give a presentation and/or visit a hospital so the children will understand that there are ways to take care of serious injuries or illnesses.
4. Contact a hospital or Poison Center for any information and educational material they may have concerning what is appropriate for children to put in their mouths or to eat.

Chapter 7
Personal Safety

5. Set up a Doctor/Hospital Center to help children become more comfortable with medical procedures. Include items such as a pillow and blanket, doctor's kit, surgical mask, "patients," "nurse," telephone, any available arm slings, splints, Velcro™ wraps, etc.

Look Sharp

1. Discuss and model safe and unsafe ways of sitting or moving about in rooms.
2. Discuss and model safe and unsafe ways of moving about outside when running, using roller blades, skateboards, etc. Emphasize the importance of looking all around you, looking where you are going and using caution on slippery, bumpy or other hazardous surfaces.
3. Teach children bicycle/tricycle safety by having them go through the process of acquiring a "driver's license." (See pages 37-42 for introductory letter, application and test and congratulatory letter and license. An application for renewal and renewal notification letters are included, if reinforcement is necessary.) After children have passed the "written" test, administer a "road" test. Use written test items as a guideline. As in real life, this license must be carried while operating any pedal vehicle. If the safety rules are not followed, the license may be "suspended" anywhere from a few minutes to the remainder of the day.

Culmination

- Award the Personal Safety Merit Badge. If a banner is being used, the children may glue it on at this time.

Chapter 7
Personal Safety

First Aid Kit Sample

Suggested Materials: construction paper (black and red), glue, cotton swabs, cotton balls, bandages, gauze, tape, tongue depressors, wipes, disposable gloves

Closed Kit

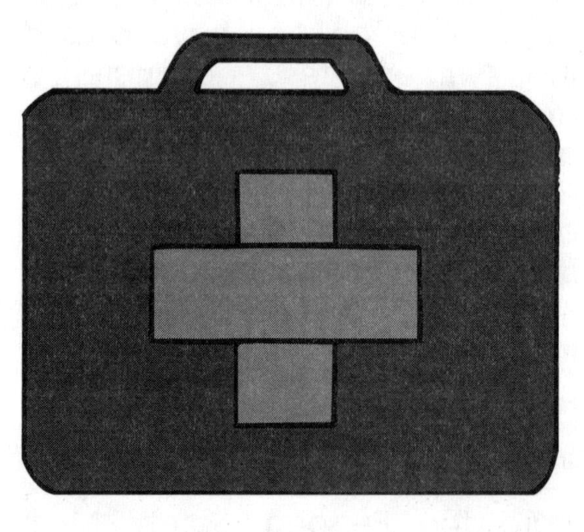

Open Kit

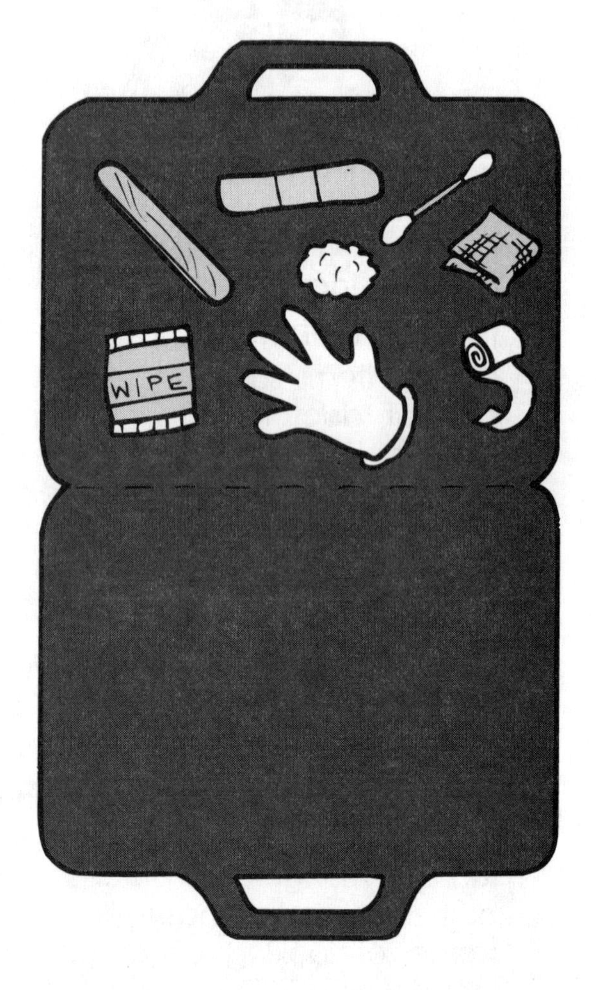

Instructions

1. Fold a 12" x 18" sheet of black construction paper in half.
2. Cut the folded black construction paper into a first aid kit.
3. Children cut two 1 1/2" x 5" strips of red construction paper for a cross.
4. Children glue red strips on outside of kit to form a cross.
5. Children open kit and glue medical supplies inside.

Name ______________________________

Chapter 7
Personal Safety

Introductory Letter

Dear ______________________________,

I understand that you are learning to operate a pedal vehicle.

You will need to apply for a Driver's License by taking the enclosed test and signing your name. Return the completed form to:

Department of Pedal Vehicles
1642 Tricycle Lane
Wheeler, USA

You will also need to show that you can ride and park your tricycle safely by passing a "road" test.

After you pass the tests, you will receive your Driver's License.

Sincerely,

E.Z. Rhodes

E.Z. Rhodes
Department of Pedal Vehicles

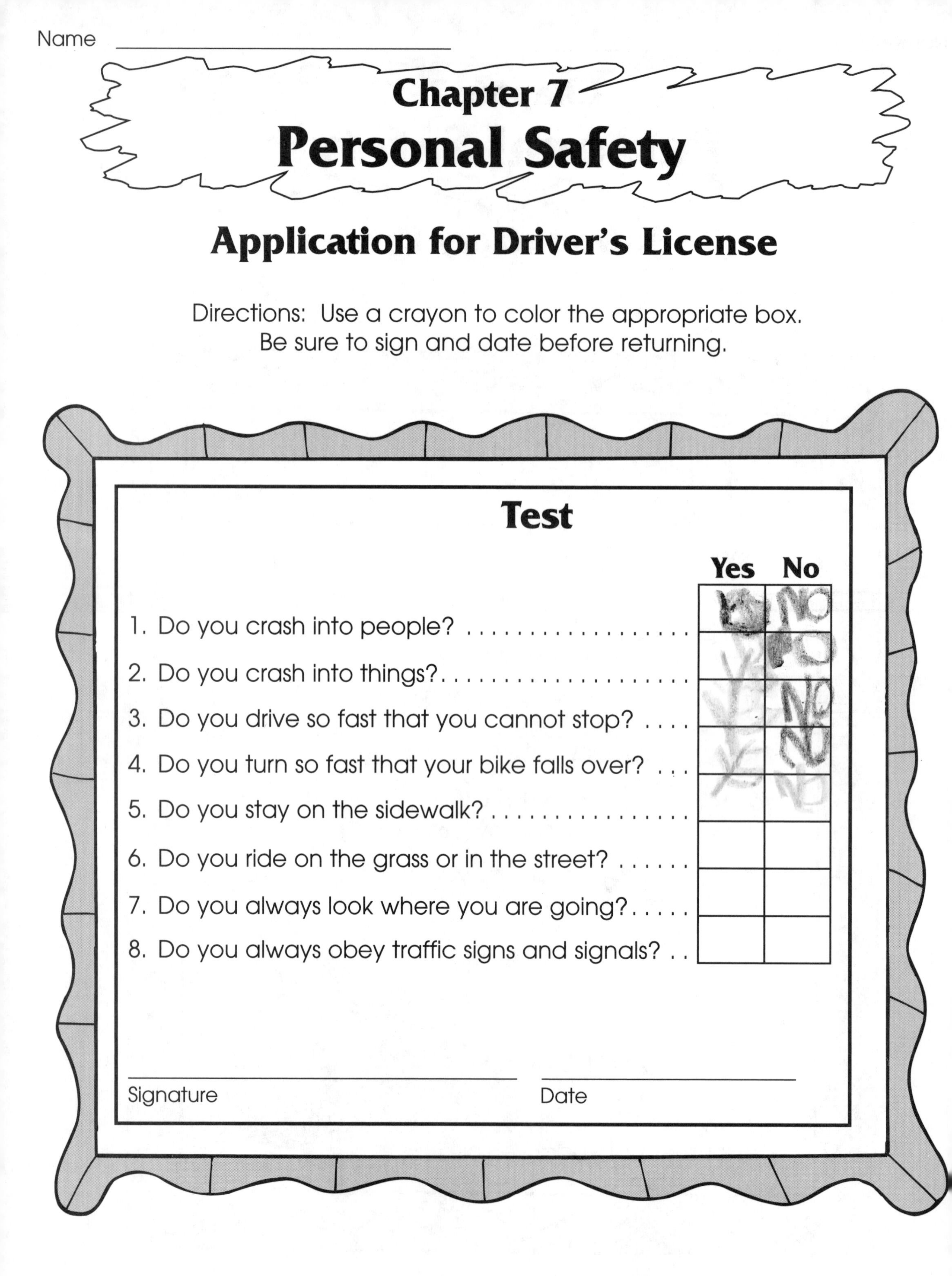

Name ______________________

Chapter 7
Personal Safety

Application for Driver's License

Directions: Use a crayon to color the appropriate box.
Be sure to sign and date before returning.

Test

	Yes	No
1. Do you crash into people?		
2. Do you crash into things?.		
3. Do you drive so fast that you cannot stop?		
4. Do you turn so fast that your bike falls over? . . .		
5. Do you stay on the sidewalk?		
6. Do you ride on the grass or in the street?		
7. Do you always look where you are going?.		
8. Do you always obey traffic signs and signals? . .		

______________________ Signature ______________________ Date

Name ____________________

Chapter 7
Personal Safety

Introductory Letter

Dear ______________________,

Congratulations! You have passed your pedal vehicle test and have shown that you can drive safely.

Your driver's license is enclosed. Be sure to carry it with you whenever you operate a pedal vehicle.

Sincerely,

E.Z. Rhodes

E.Z. Rhodes
Department of Pedal Vehicles

Name ____________________

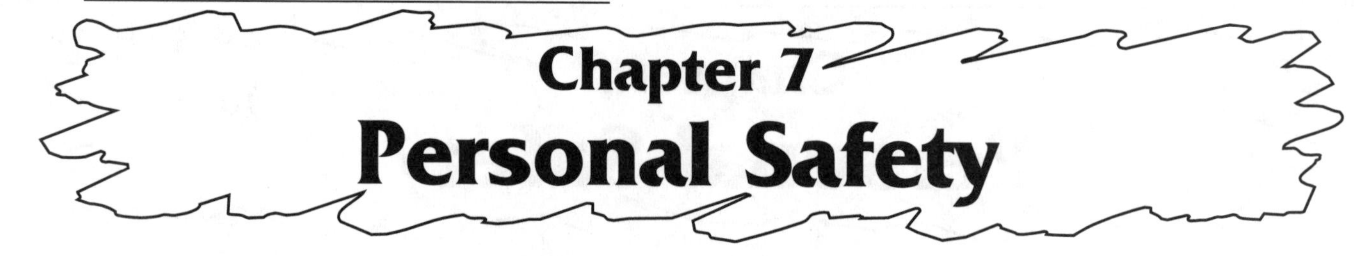

Chapter 7
Personal Safety

Driver's License

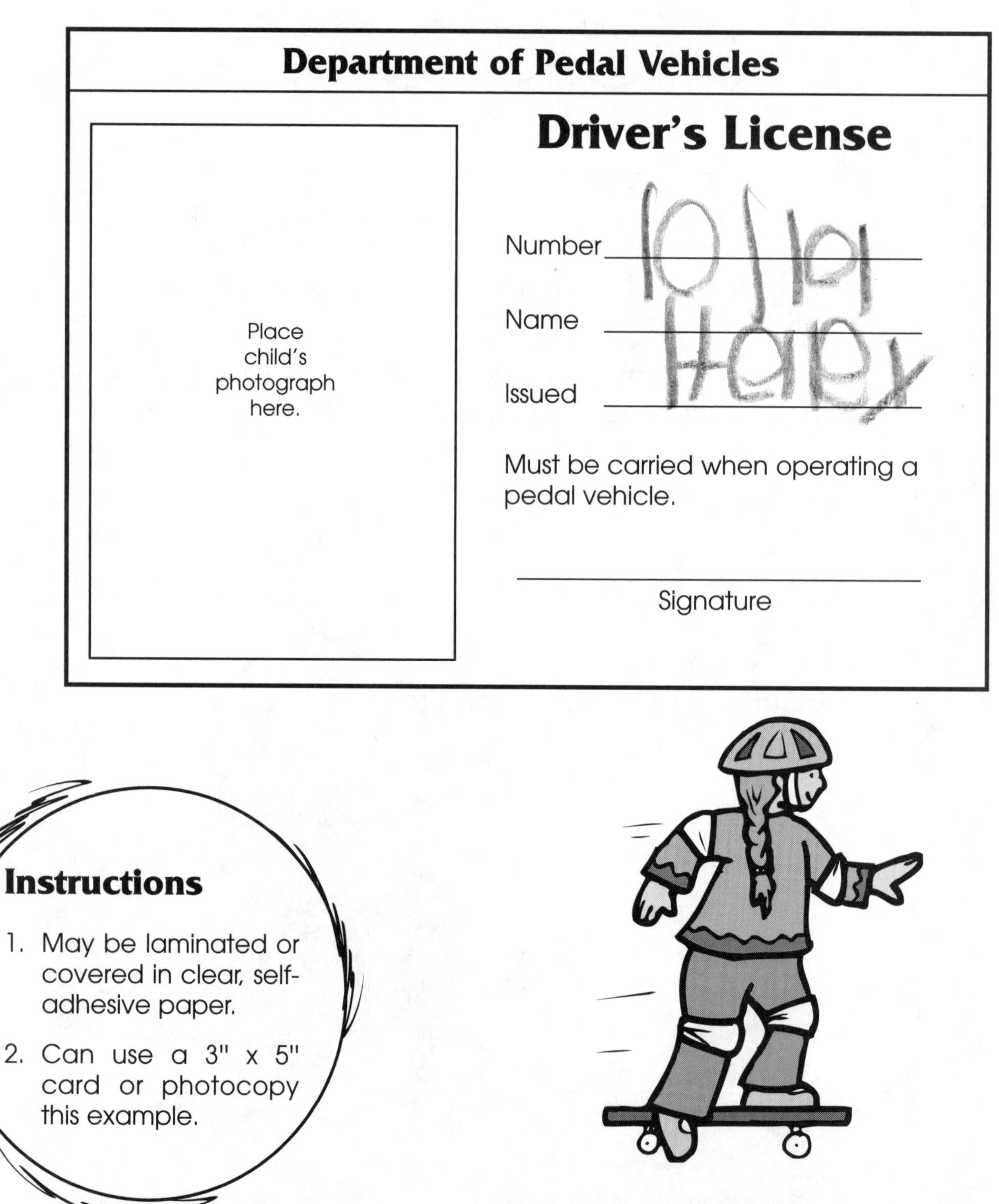

Department of Pedal Vehicles

Place child's photograph here.

Driver's License

Number ____________________

Name ____________________

Issued ____________________

Must be carried when operating a pedal vehicle.

____
Signature

Instructions

1. May be laminated or covered in clear, self-adhesive paper.
2. Can use a 3" x 5" card or photocopy this example.

Name ______________________________

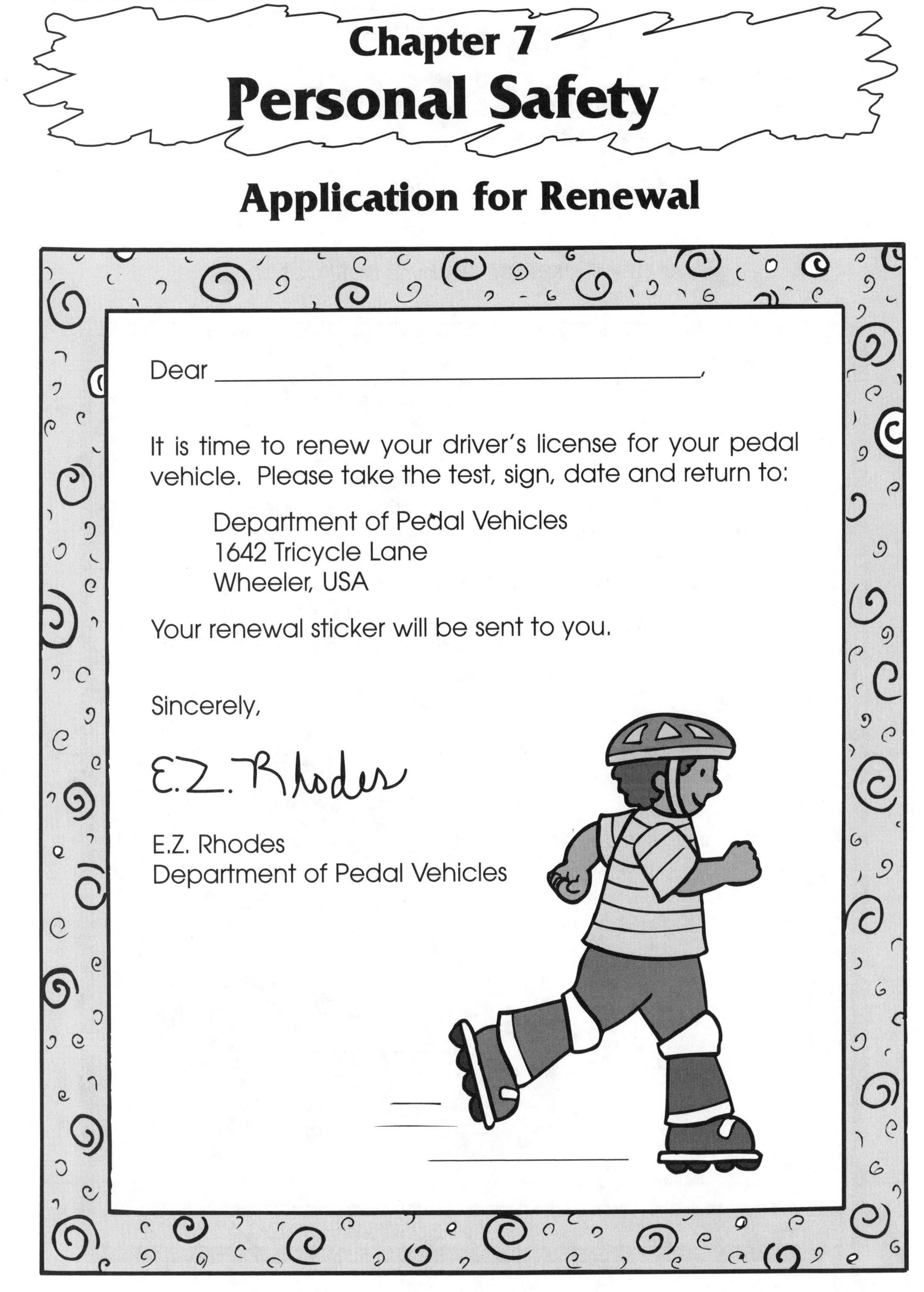

Chapter 7
Personal Safety

Application for Renewal

Dear ______________________________,

It is time to renew your driver's license for your pedal vehicle. Please take the test, sign, date and return to:

Department of Pedal Vehicles
1642 Tricycle Lane
Wheeler, USA

Your renewal sticker will be sent to you.

Sincerely,

E.Z. Rhodes

E.Z. Rhodes
Department of Pedal Vehicles

Name ______________________________

Chapter 7
Personal Safety

Renewal Notification

Use any sticker for renewal notification.

Dear ____,

Congratulations! You have passed your pedal vehicle test and your license has been renewed.

Enclosed is your renewal sticker. Please place it on the back of your license and be sure to carry it with you whenever you operate a pedal vehicle.

Sincerely,

E.Z. Rhodes

E.Z. Rhodes
Department of Pedal Vehicles

Chapter 8
Safety with Others

Problems

- Pushing when lining up, standing in line, playing a game, etc.
- Throwing rocks, sand or other objects.
- Running or bumping into others.

Goals

- Increase awareness of actions that could be harmful to others.
- Care about the consequences of harmful actions.
- Act responsibly.

Chapter 8
Safety with Others

Ways & Means

Earn a Merit Badge

- Introduce the children to the specific area of safety with others and explain to them that they may earn a Safety with Others Merit Badge. (See page 23 for pattern.)

Model/Role Play

- Act out situations which demonstrate safe and unsafe behaviors. (Refer to Problems and Goals on page 43 for examples.)

Don Your Hat

- Children make a "Use Your Head" hat. (See page 45 for sample.) They may wear their hats at the beginning of the day as a reminder to be safe with others or at the end of the day as a reward for responsible behavior.

All Around the Town

- Encourage the children to practice safety on a playground, in a play room, waiting in a line, in a crowd or in other real-life situations. Observe and praise their efforts to act responsibly.

Culmination

- Award the Safety with Others Merit Badge. If a banner is being used, the children may glue it on at this time.

Name ______________________

Chapter 8
Safety with Others

"Use Your Head" Hat Sample

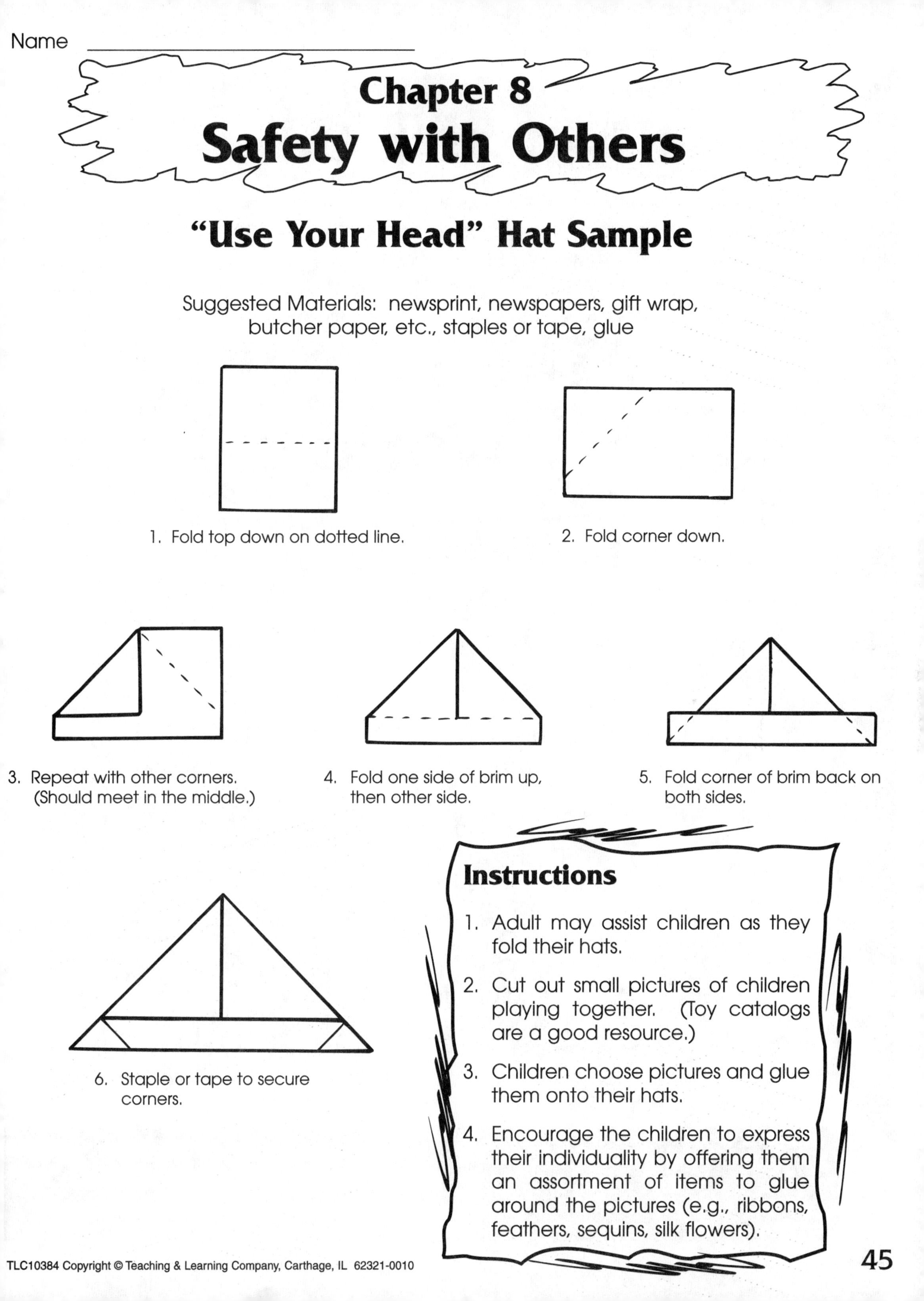

Suggested Materials: newsprint, newspapers, gift wrap, butcher paper, etc., staples or tape, glue

1. Fold top down on dotted line.
2. Fold corner down.
3. Repeat with other corners. (Should meet in the middle.)
4. Fold one side of brim up, then other side.
5. Fold corner of brim back on both sides.
6. Staple or tape to secure corners.

Instructions

1. Adult may assist children as they fold their hats.
2. Cut out small pictures of children playing together. (Toy catalogs are a good resource.)
3. Children choose pictures and glue them onto their hats.
4. Encourage the children to express their individuality by offering them an assortment of items to glue around the pictures (e.g., ribbons, feathers, sequins, silk flowers).

Unit 3

The Larger World

Social Growth

Baa, baa, black sheep,
Have you any wool?
Yes, sir, yes, sir,
Three bags full:
One for the master,
One for the dame,
And one for the little boy,
Who lives down the lane.

—Mother Goose

Chapter 9

Litterbug Lookout

Problems

- Unaware of the reciprocal relationship between self and the environment.
- Discard trash carelessly.

Goals

- Become aware of the importance of the role people play in changing the environment.
- Distinguish man-made litter from fallen leaves, twigs, etc.
- Learn about the recycling process (nature's and man's).
- Take responsibility for disposing of trash in appropriate places.
- Develop a sense of pride by contributing to environmental cleanups.

Chapter 9
Litterbug Lookout

Ways & Means

Go on a Scavenger Hunt

- Introduce the word *environment* to the children and explain it as the world we live in. Give examples of things in the environment which are natural and others that are man-made.
- Make each of the children a Scavenger Hunt Checklist. (See page 50.)
- Distribute checklists and tell the children that we are going on a hunt. We will all look for the items on the list. (Encourage the children to look for items that are not listed but that are a part of the environment.) If the children notice any litter, identify it as a harmful part of our environment that we will talk more about later.

The World Around Me

- Talk about changes we make in the environment (e.g., making footprints in the dirt or sand; planting and caring for flowers, vegetables and trees; littering). Then relate these to the changes the environment makes on us (e.g., footprints are erased by water; trees and plants provide food and shade; litter harms the water we drink and the air we breathe).
- Prepare a "The World Around Me" poster/mobile for each child. (See sample on page 51.)
- The children use their own ideas to create and complete their individual poster/mobile.

Catch a Litterbug

- Prepare a Litterbug. (See sample on page 53.)
- Redefine man-made litter and talk about some of its harmful effects on the environment.
- Prepare an area in your classroom in which to collect litter. Scatter the litter items (see page 52) on the floor. Set out five paper garbage sacks labeled: *Recycle: Glass, Recycle: Paper, Recycle: Metal, Recycle: Plastic and Trash*.
- When all the "litter" has been collected, have children identify which items go into the recycle containers and which go into the trash.
- Give the children the prepared "bugs" and follow the instructions on page 53.
- Display litterbugs as a reminder to the children to throw trash in appropriate containers and participate in environmental cleanups.

Chapter 9
Litterbug Lookout

Build a Thing-a-Ma-Jig

- Develop the children's concepts of nature's ways versus man's way of recycling. Explain that nature often helps our world as it takes care of its litter (e.g., fallen leaves enrich the soil, branches and logs become food and homes for many animals and insects). Brainstorm with the children about ways we can recycle our man-made litter.
- Encourage creative recycling by helping children save small juice cans, boxes, lids, Styrofoam™ pieces, plastic forks and spoons, etc.
- Provide the children with a cardboard base and allow them to glue on collected items to create a Thing-A-Ma-Jig. If necessary, suggest possibilities such as creating a city, a building, a robot, a spaceship, strange creatures or any other Thing-a-Ma-Jig.
- Provide paint for the children to decorate their projects.

Make a Silk Purse Out of a Sow's Ear

- Puppets out of small milk cartons.
- Candles out of crayon pieces.
- Multicolored crayons out of melted crayon pieces.
- Papier-mâché sculpture out of old newspapers.
- Mobiles or sculptures out of broken radios, clocks or toy pieces.
- Stationery out of old newspaper or gift wrap pulp.

Culmination

- Award the children personal wastebaskets. These wastebaskets can be made from large ice cream, popcorn or fried chicken containers which may be obtained from local merchants upon request. An adult may paint or decorate the containers or give them to the children with materials to decorate.

Reinforcement

- Call attention to the important role we all play in protecting the environment by talking about it whenever involved in acts of litter disposal, recycling and general conservation.

Name ____________________

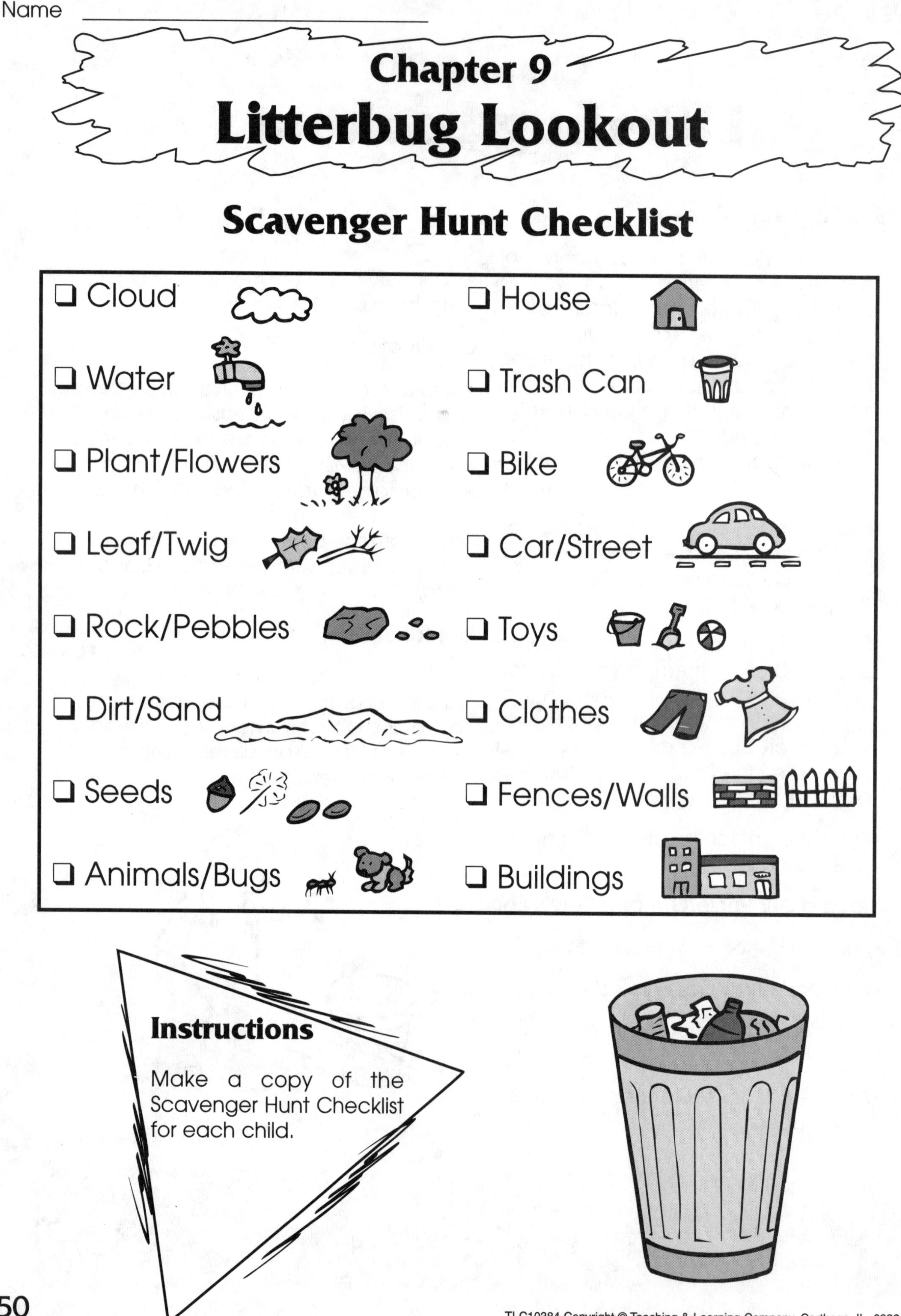

Chapter 9
Litterbug Lookout

Scavenger Hunt Checklist

❑ Cloud	❑ House
❑ Water	❑ Trash Can
❑ Plant/Flowers	❑ Bike
❑ Leaf/Twig	❑ Car/Street
❑ Rock/Pebbles	❑ Toys
❑ Dirt/Sand	❑ Clothes
❑ Seeds	❑ Fences/Walls
❑ Animals/Bugs	❑ Buildings

Instructions

Make a copy of the Scavenger Hunt Checklist for each child.

Name ___________________________

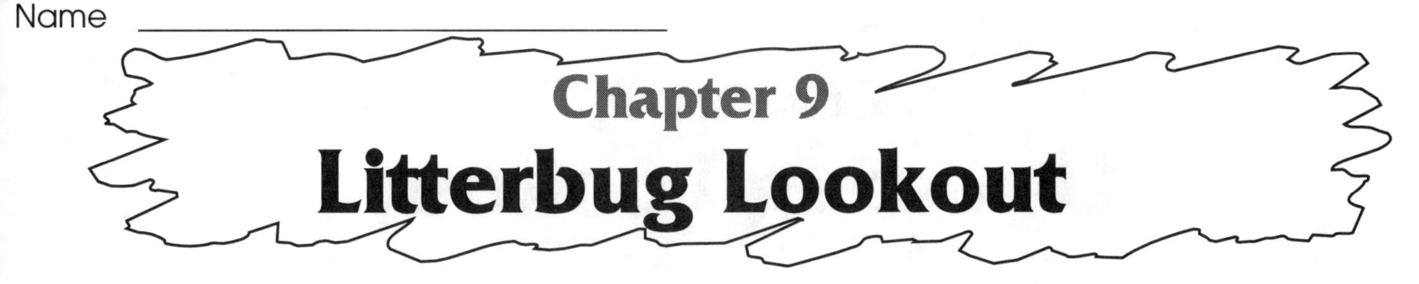

"The World Around Me" Poster/Mobile Sample

Suggested Materials: tagboard or paper plate, crayons or photograph, glue

Instructions

1. Use a paper plate or cut tagboard into circles.
2. Draw a small circle in center.
3. Divide the large circle into six sections.
4. Children draw their own face in the small circle or glue on a photograph of themselves.
5. Children glue on items found on the scavenger hunt and/or color, cut and glue pictures from the list on the checklist one page 50.
6. Display in the room.

Optional: Use both sides of circle and hang it as a mobile.

Name ______________________________

Chapter 9
Litterbug Lookout

Items for Litterbug Cleanup

Name ______________________________

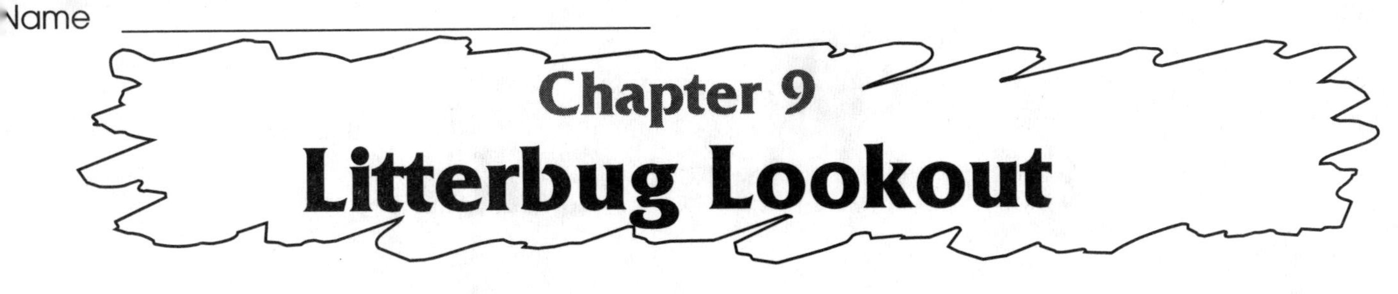

Chapter 9
Litterbug Lookout

Litterbug Sample

Suggested Materials: paper plate or colored construction paper, glue, litter from bag

Instructions

1. If not using a paper plate for the body, cut a body out of construction paper.
2. Cut six long strips of a contrasting color of construction paper for the legs.
3. Cut out two antennae.
4. Children fold the legs and glue them on the body.
5. Children glue on the antennae.
6. Children then glue small pieces of litter onto the bug's body.

Optional: Legs and antennae may be glued on by an adult.

Chapter 10
Friendship Quilt

Problem

- Unaware of opportunities or ways to make a difference in the lives of people who are homeless.

Goals

- Care about the needs of others.
- Learn that there are ways to reach out and make a difference in people's lives.
- Experience the joy of helping others.
- Empower self through good deeds.

Chapter 10
Friendship Quilt

Ways & Means

• A particularly appropriate time for these projects is during the fall and winter holidays in order to counteract some of the "hard core" commercialism to which children are exposed.

Friendship Quilt

1. Premake specific items necessary for this project. (See instructions, patterns and samples on pages 56-57.)
2. Introduce the children to the fact that some people may suffer from the cold because they do not have warm homes. Tell them there are ways we can all help to solve this problem.
3. Explain that one way to help people keep warm is by contributing blankets.
4. Show the children the boy and girl who need blankets to keep them warm. Then show them the package containing the blankets.
5. Set up the package, and the boy and girl as shown on page 57.
6. Each time the children contribute their quilt square, move the package closer to the children.
7. When all quilt squares have been turned in, the children unwrap the package and cover the boy and girl with the blankets.

The House That "Habitat" Built

1. Observe and talk about animal habitats or homes found in places such as parks, pet stores and zoos. Nests, trees, rocks, shells, webs and burrows are examples of homes that are easily found.
2. Ask the children why both animals and people need homes. Important points to cover include home as a place:

   a. to be protected form wind, rain, heat and cold
   b. to be with your family
   c. to get clean, eat, sleep and play
   d. to keep your food, clothes and toys

3. Guide discussion to help children realize that there are some people who do not have these securities because they have become homeless. Tell them that one way people can help solve this problem is by building houses. (You may wish to introduce the children to Habitat for Humanity or check the library for local charitable organizations that have similar programs.)
4. As a concrete representation of their concern, the children may each build a birdhouse. (See page 60.)
5. When complete, hang the finished birdhouse outside, or let the children take them home.

Culmination

• Provide large cardboard boxes for the children to build play homes. The children's interest will determine the complexity of this activity. They may build homes by simply stacking boxes or by cutting out doors and windows, painting and decorating.

Chapter 10
Friendship Quilt

Magic Blankets Directions

Suggested Materials: colored tagboard; manila construction paper; felt tip markers (fine); 9" x 9" piece of blanket material (cut in half); brown wrapping paper; tape; string; "stamp" for postage; paper clip; pins or tacks

Instructions

1. Using patterns on page 57, cut out the boy and girl and fill in the details with fine-tipped felt markers or use paper dolls.
2. Fold the "blankets" wrap them with brown paper; tape the package together and address it for "mailing" using "stamp" for postage.
3. Set up in room so that the children will see the progress of the blanket package as it travels to its destination.
4. Hang a string across a designated area.
5. Attach a paper clip to the top of the package so it can move.

Optional: In lieu of string, use pin or tape to move the package.

Chapter 10
Friendship Quilt

Magic Blankets Patterns

Chapter 10
Friendship Quilt

You Will Need

1. Square of white fabric for each child (about 8" x 8"-10" x 10") Note: Fabric with some polyester content seems to hold the fabric marker color better and will shrink less when washed.
2. Additional squares to even out the pattern.
3. Fabric markers in bright colors.
4. Batting for inside the quilt.
5. Fabric for the back (size to be determined by number of squares and pattern then add 12" to top and side measurements).
6. Thread and yarn.

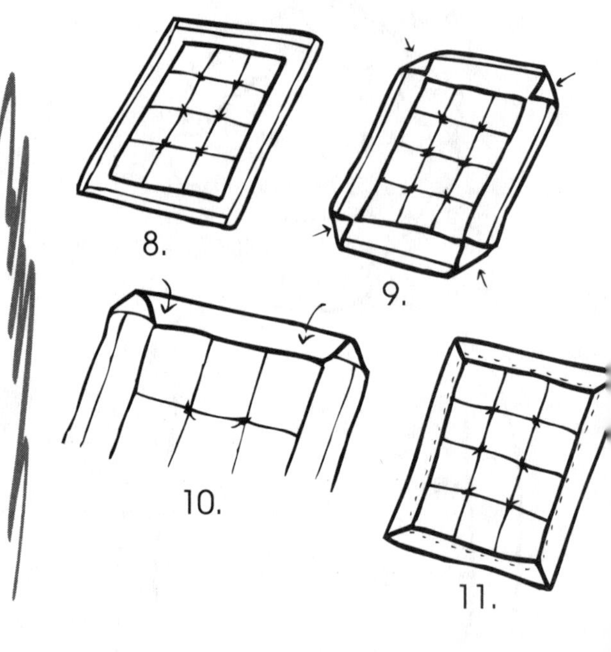

Instructions

1. Give each child a fabric square to color. Designs may be original.
2. When all squares have been received, arrange into even rows. (You may have to add some squares to make this come out even.) Let children help you arrange the squares in a pleasing pattern.
3. Sew the squares together in rows, then sew the rows together. (It is helpful to press open the seams at each step.)
4. Measure your quilt top. Lay out batting to fit.
5. Add 12" to the top and side measurements and cut the fabric for the back. Place wrong side up.
6. Center the batting on the backing fabric. (You should have 6" extra fabric all around.) Place the quilt top (right side up) on top of the batting.
7. Thread a large needle with yarn, take a stitch through the batting and backing, knot and tie off at every corner.
8. Fold fabric down 1/2" all around the backing material.
9. Fold down corners.
10. Bring folded edge of backing fabric over raw edge of quilt top and machine or hand stitch into place.
11. Admire your handiwork!

Chapter 10
Friendship Quilt

The House That "Habitat" Built

Suggested Materials: half-gallon milk carton or plastic container; different colored self-sticking stickers; cord; pencil-sized doweling; scissors or knife

Instructions

1. Children wash containers.
2. Cut out the opening, slits for dowel and holes for cord. (See sample.)
3. Children decorate the birdhouse with self-sticking stickers.
4. Children insert the dowel.
5. Children attach cord to the birdhouse with help as needed.

Milk Carton

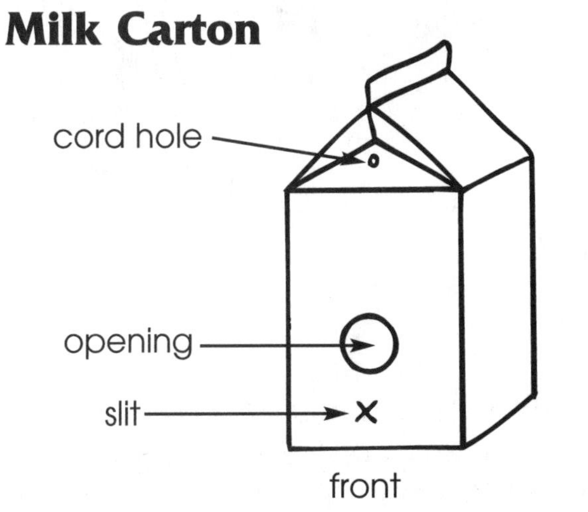

front

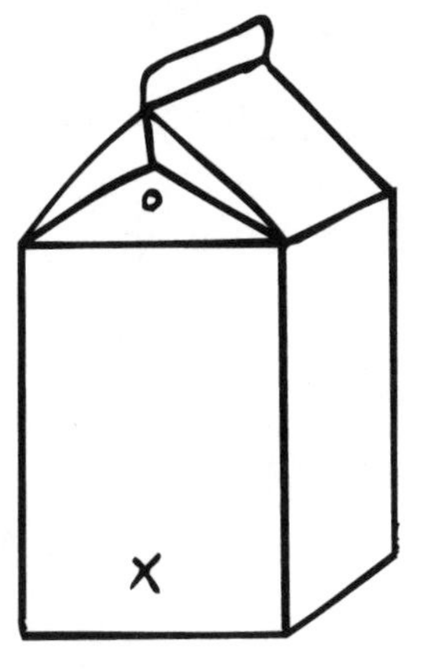
back

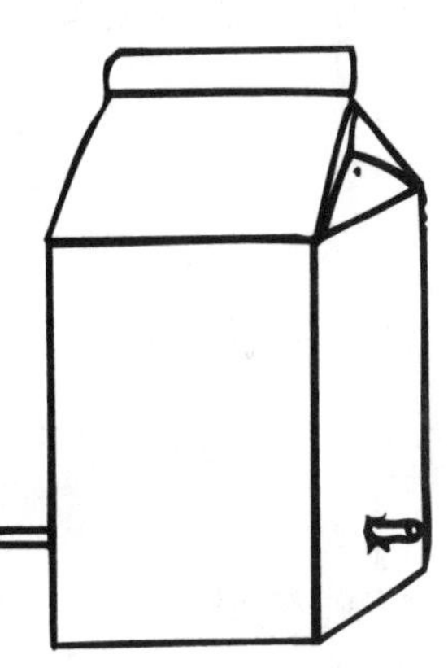
side

Plastic Container

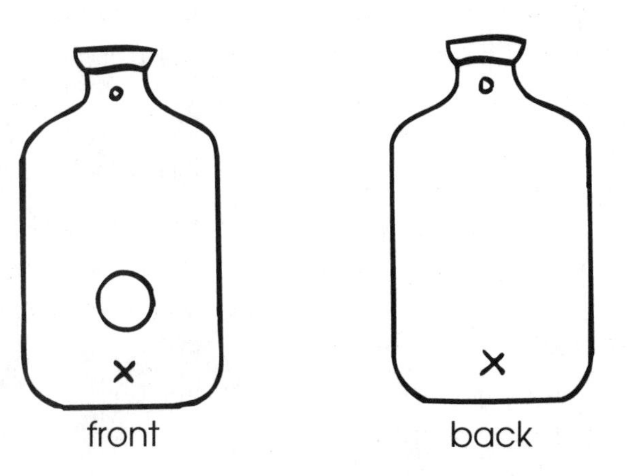
front back

Chapter 11
Friendship Soup

Problems

- Unaware of opportunities or ways to make a difference in the lives of people who are hungry.

Goals

- Care about the needs of others.
- Learn that there are ways to reach out and make a difference in people's lives.
- Experience the joy of helping others.
- Empower self through good deeds.

Chapter 11
Friendship Soup

Ways & Means

- In this activity, children will contribute the ingredients needed to prepare vegetable soup and donate it to the hungry. In advance, you will need to contact a local soup kitchen or agency that provides meals to shut-ins or the homeless. You may encounter regulations that will make it impossible to bring in prepared food. In that case, have children contribute canned goods instead of fresh, to donate to the organization.
- A particularly appropriate time for this project is during the fall and winter holidays in order to counteract some of the excessive commercialism to which children are exposed.

Friendship Soup

1. Premake the recipe cards (See page 63.)
2. Introduce the children to the fact that many people in the world are hungry.
3. Explain that one way to help is to contribute food to a local agency or shelter.
4. Give each of the children a recipe card. Talk about the different items that are pictured on the cards. Can children identify all the items? Discuss the things with which they may not be familiar.
5. Can children guess what they will do with these items? Record their responses.

Eat them!	|||
Make soup.	||
Give away.	||||

6. Plan a Friendship Soup-Making Day.
   - If you are able to cook the soup in your school or classroom, make arrangements to have all the necessary utensils and equipment at hand. (For example, soup pot, measuring cups and spoons, cutting boards and knives*, can openers, etc.)
   - If you have to do the cooking elsewhere but can prepare the ingredients, you might need to have on hand: cutting boards and utensils*, measuring cups and spoons, plastic bags for storage, etc.
   - If you are going to donate canned goods, you will need collection bags or boxes. Perhaps your students would like to prepare adhesive labels for the cans which might say, "A gift from Mrs. Johnson's class at Washington School."

*All cutting activities are to be performed by adults.

Chapter 11

Friendship Soup

- Encourage children to wear or bring aprons, smocks, chef's hats (pattern on page 64), oven mitts, etc. If time or enthusiasm permits, you might want to ad lib a song as you prepare (or pack) the ingredients. For example:

  "This is the way we make our soup, make our soup, make our soup—

  This is the way we make our soup, to feed the hungry people!"

  "This is the way we cut the carrots, cut the carrots, cut the carrots—

  This is the way we cut the carrots, to feed the hungry people!"

  Etc.

7. Explain that one way to help is to contribute food to a local agency.
8. Give each of the children a recipe card. Talk about the different items listed on the cards. Can children guess what they will do with these items?
9. Record children's answers.

Name ______________________

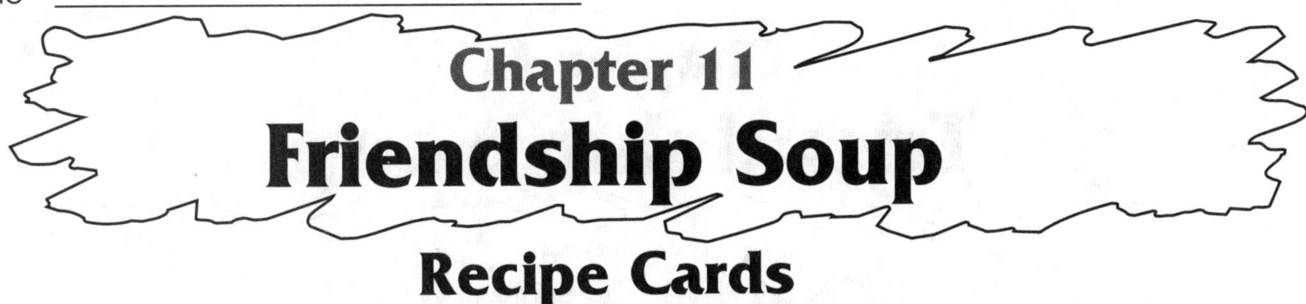

Chapter 11
Friendship Soup

Recipe Cards

This recipe makes about 6 cups. If you have more children than cards, you can double the ingredients. Adjust seasoning to taste. Omit the ground beef if you want to make a vegetarian version and use vegetable broth.

Brown the beef in a small amount of oil. Add broth and water. Add vegetables. Cook until vegetables are tender. Add alphabets.

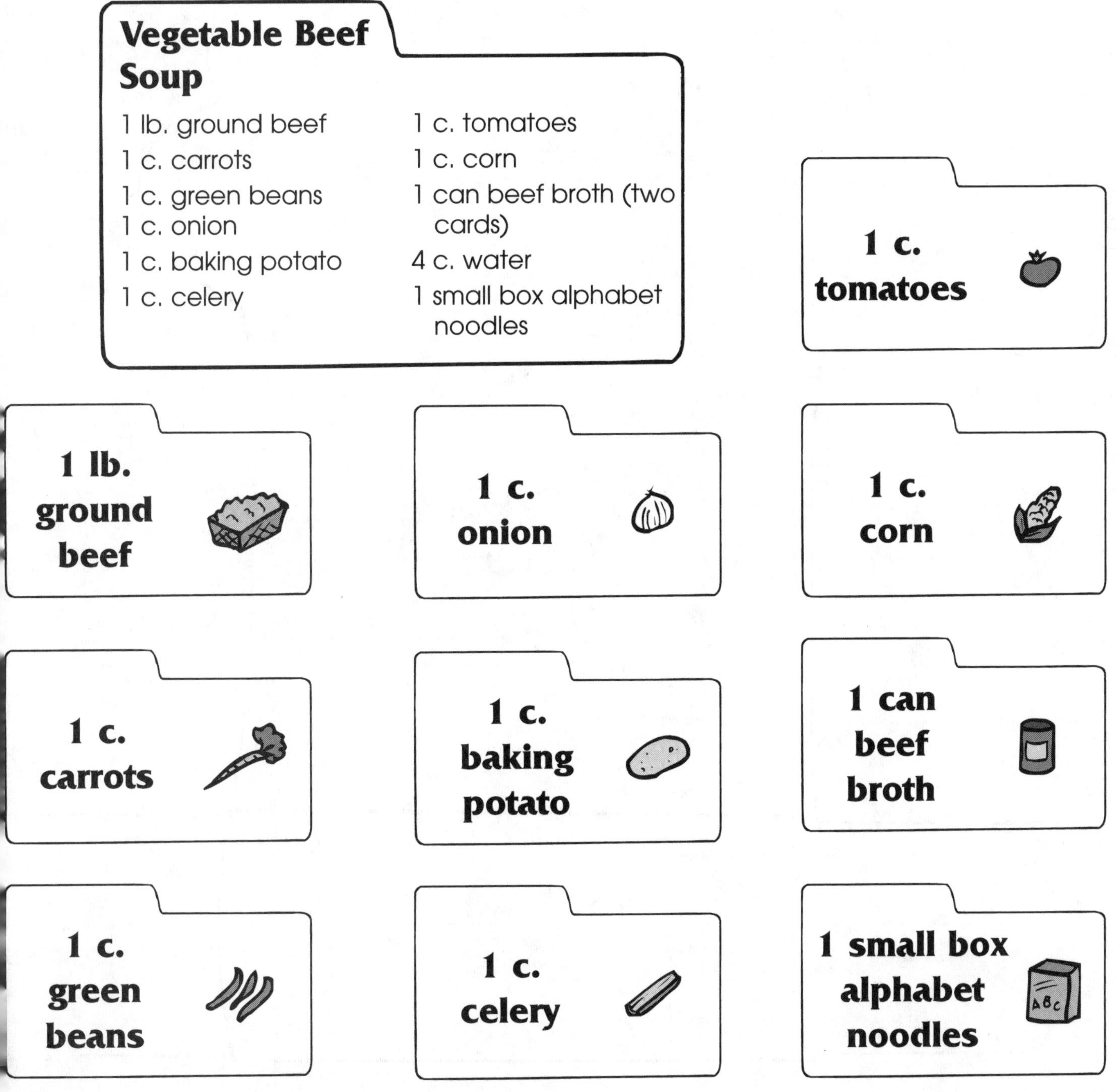

Vegetable Beef Soup

1 lb. ground beef
1 c. carrots
1 c. green beans
1 c. onion
1 c. baking potato
1 c. celery
1 c. tomatoes
1 c. corn
1 can beef broth (two cards)
4 c. water
1 small box alphabet noodles

1 c. tomatoes

1 lb. ground beef

1 c. onion

1 c. corn

1 c. carrots

1 c. baking potato

1 can beef broth

1 c. green beans

1 c. celery

1 small box alphabet noodles

Chapter 11
Friendship Soup

Chef Hat Pattern

Enlarge chef hat on your photocopier to desired size.